RECREATION
FOR
BLIND ADULTS

RECREATION FOR BLIND ADULTS

Organized Programs in Specialized Settings

By

MAURICE CASE, ~~Ed.D., A.C.S.W.~~
Hunter College, University of the City of New York
Manager, Recreation and Camping Services
New York Association for the Blind
New York, New York

With Forewords by

MORTON THOMPSON, Ed.D.
National Recreation Association

EDITH L. BALL
New York University

MILTON A. GABRIELSEN
New York University

CHARLES C THOMAS · PUBLISHER
Springfield · Illinois · U.S.A.

Published and Distributed Throughout the World by

CHARLES C THOMAS • PUBLISHER

BANNERSTONE HOUSE

301-327 East Lawrence Avenue, Springfield, Illinois, U.S.A.

NATCHEZ PLANTATION HOUSE

735 North Atlantic Boulevard, Fort Lauderdale, Florida, U.S.A.

Library of Congress Catalog Card Number: 65-20836

With THOMAS BOOKS careful attention is given to all details of manufacturing and design. It is the Publisher's desire to present books that are satisfactory as to their physical qualities and artistic possibilities and appropriate for their particular use. THOMAS BOOKS will be true to those laws of quality that assure a good name and good will.

Printed in the United States of America

Y-2

To my beloved son, Lieutenant Stephen Michael Case, U.S.N., who died in line of duty in the service of his country while this book was being written to better serve people who are blind; and to my other son, Robert Ian Case, who so staunchly sustained his bereaved parents while the shock of inscrutable fate slowly receded until time and faith and until more faith and time made living again tolerable; and to my wife, Phyllis Eleanor Case, without whose body, strength, and stability, we would not be.

The common problem
Yours, mine, everyone's
Is not to fancy what
Were fair in life
Provided it could be.
But finding first
What may be, then find
How to make it fair
Up to our means.

BROWNING

FOREWORDS

RECREATION FOR BLIND ADULTS is a long overdue book dedicated to the recreational needs of our blind citizens.

Most of the literature pertaining to this subject is confined to articles and pamphlets making it a difficult task to collect adequate program materials when needed.

This book provides, under one cover, comprehensive information concerning organization, administration and program development in recreation for the blind.

Dr. Maurice Case, with his many years of practical experience in this field of specialization, has produced a text which meets a great need and which will make a vital contribution to the resource information in the field of recreation for the ill and handicapped.

MORTON THOMPSON, ED. D.
Director, Consulting Service on Recreation for the Ill and Handicapped
National Recreation Association

IN THIS AGE, the problems that increasing leisure presents to the total society obscures and diminishes the problems that it presents to the disabled in our midst. Those with handicaps traditionally have been under-served. Now, when so many have so many leisure needs, there are those who consider that the disabled minority must wait for services until the problems of the majority have been served. These people fail to realize that leisure needs relate to all people whether able-bodied or non-able-bodied. They must be met through the provision of both public and private resources and must be based on the needs of the group. All people need recreational experiences in leisure and the community must find the way to provide them.

This manual, outlining how some needs of the blind may be met through the provision of special center services, is a sensitive and creative approach to the problem. The author, with years of experience in this field, brings a wealth of knowledge to the subject and lays it against a background of understanding of sociological and psychological problems involved. With this frame of reference, Maurice Case presents practical material which, at the same time, is scholarly. It should serve as an excellent source not only for those who work in centers for the blind but also those who work with the blind, or the handicapped generally, in other settings.

EDITH L. BALL
Associate Professor
New York University

SOCIAL INSTITUTIONS arise as necessary instrumentalities to serve the basic and derived needs of individuals and their communities. Organized recreation programs are age-old and universal, conducted in ancient temples, in monasteries of the middle ages, in jungle tribal squares or in modern centers. The human need for change, balance, self-expression and relationship cannot be thwarted without dire consequences for the individual and for his community.

Since time immemorial blindness has lamentably conjured up within the sighted fearful visions of mutilated bodies and minds. The inevitable reaction has been rejection and ostracism. For both the handicapped and sighted, blindness reciprocally became synonomous with isolation. Rejected, alone, inactive, an individual withers, along with his community.

While awaiting a more enlightened era when maimed humanity may engender a more mature concern, specialized programs have developed to provide some opportunities for blind individuals to experience the many human satisfactions derived from participation in recreation activities. Aside from the humanistic considerations, preventive and therapeutic concomitants of recreation participation are incalculable.

Maurice Case has devoted his life to serving the blind. His accomplishments have given him national recognition. As an accredited recreator and certified social worker, Dr. Case bridges the chasm between theoretical conceptions and practice within a framework of achievable objectives and goals. *Recreation for Blind Adults* will serve as a valuable primer for practitioners concerned with the welfare of visually impaired persons and the communities of which they are an inextricable part.

MILTON A. GABRIELSEN
Professor of Education
New York University

PREFACE

THE CONTENT of *Recreation for Blind Adults* is the product of more than thirty years of pragmatic experiences in specialized services for blind individuals. From 1955 through 1961, these learnings were continuously supplemented by attendance at formal university graduate courses which served to give them more significant form and meaning. In 1963, the data were crystallized and synthesized through a descriptive-status doctoral study of the major specialized recreation centers for blind adults in New York City.

Organized recreation programs in special settings are preventive and therapeutic social instrumentalities for maintaining and enhancing the mental and physical well-being of blind individuals, and of the communities of which they are an integral part. This assertion rests upon a positive and fundamental principle, i.e., that the essential purpose of our democratic society should be the furtherance of individual self-realization through opportunities for activities and experiences which liberate and satisfy the basic needs of every member of the community. Implicitly, this ideal goes even beyond equality of opportunity, and makes us all more fully responsible for each other—and for ourselves.

As a professional discipline, organized recreation derives social sanction through the recognition of common basic human needs, and the commitment to constructively meet these needs within a humanitarian concern for every individual's right to appropriate opportunities for activities and experiences which make life more purposeful and worthwhile. Indeed, in our increasingly leisure-centered society, recreation, organized and unorganized, has earned high priority as a desirable modality for meeting individual and community needs.

The direct relationship between discrete, identifiable human needs and their satisfaction through recreation activities and experiences has given rise to the incisive term "recreation needs."

Professional literature is replete with references to the commonality of human recreation needs. The phrase has had legalistic recognition, e.g., the New York State Education Law, Article 24, Section 1120, 1956, explicitly and inclusively states that "recreation is a basic human need."

Inspirational exhortations notwithstanding, everyday experiences strengthen the assumption that blindness is a severe and disabling condition which significantly limits and restricts opportunities for participation in satisfying activities and experiences; and at a time when many needs are heightened through a multiplicity of interacting intrinsic and extrinsic effects of the handicap. Traumatic shock and fear immobilize not only the individual, but also the community. Unless the processes of rehabilitation and habilitation begin and continue, sad and costly debilitation is inevitable for the blind individual and for those around him.

Of course, some blind persons with sufficient inner strengths and resources who reside in communities with adequate helping services are soon enabled to function again in non-specialized settings, at home, at work, and at recreation. Workers in the social science professions generally agree that the better life is the open life in the mainstream of community activities. However, general principles concerning integration have tended to obscure the ironic reality that for many blind persons, community opportunities for participation in organized recreation, specialized or not, are largely non-existent—even for those relatively more adequate individuals able to risk the slings and arrows of age-old prejudices in a mobile world basically structured around visual perception. Even with professional assistance, many blind individuals continue to require specialized community services in order to maintain psychological and physical health. Every community, or group of contiguous communities, should have a committee of citizens charged with the responsibility for inquiring into, and planning for the recreation needs of their isolated and inactive blind residents—through public and/or through private auspices.

Professional Recreation has delineated a number of categories of activities like arts and crafts, dance, dramatics, group activities, literary and language classes, music, nature study and outings, social events, sports and games, and others. Scores of discrete activities may be developed in each category. Recreation activities should be designed to meet the numerous and varied needs of the participants.

Clearly implicit in specialization is the presumption that the regular or usual is somehow and/or somewhat altered to meet differences in interest, abilities and capacities. In this context, knowledge and skill in non-specialized organized recreation is largely presumed, and this book is intended for those workers already reasonably competent in regular organized recreation operations. The book is concerned primarily with organized programs in specialized recreation centers for blind adults. The content, however, is generally applicable to other settings where the health and welfare of blind individuals are of concern, *viz.*, regular community centers and settlement houses where relatively more adequate visually handicapped persons are encouraged to participate in activities which do not require too much vision; centers and clubs for older citizens among whom the incidence of visual impairment tends to be high; residential homes, hospitals, and custodial institutions where numbers of blind folks are located; and the hundreds of smaller specialized agencies for the blind which include recreation as an occasional and limited service. Also, there are much useful data for the families and friends of persons who are blind.

Ultimately, every institution, formal or informal, is a function of community needs and is measured by the quality and effectiveness of its practice in relation to those needs. This volume should help to clarify the meaning of blindness to many folks, blind and sighted, and raise the levels of recreation achievements in specialized as well as in non-specialized settings. As with all social constructs, the tyranny of the blindness stereotypes can be obliterated most effectively by exposures, and by the values and ideas derived from direct human experiences, for both blind and sighted persons.

MAURICE CASE

ACKNOWLEDGMENTS

THANKS for invaluable assistance should go to so many individuals for their help and encouragement with the preparation of the manuscript:

To Eva Wells who so conscientiously typed and retyped hundreds of pages, all the while telling the author how much she enjoyed reading the material;

To my secretaries at the New York Lighthouse, Isabel Belotti and Nancy Ford who generously volunteered their overtime to edit and make corrections;

To Malcom Parkhurst, Lighthouse volunteer worker and amateur photographer whose pictures add so much to the quality of the presentation;

Finally, thanks to the corporate entity, The New York Association for the Blind, The Lighthouse, in which environs occurred so many of the experiences that form the core of the contents.

M.C.

CONTENTS

Page

Forewords—Morton Thompson, Edith L. Ball and Milton A. Gabrielsen vii

Preface xi

Acknowledgments xv

Chapter

I. Blindness 3

Incidence; Prevalence; Forecast 3

Definition 3

The Legally Blind with Usable Vision 5

II. Historical Background 7

Recreation Programs for Blind Adults 13

III. Recreation and Social Group Work 15

Professional Recreation 15

Basic Human Needs; Basic Recreation Needs 16

Social Group Work 20

Common Elements in Recreation and Social Group Work 23

IV. The Impact of Blindness 24

Intrinsic and Extrinsic Effects of Blindness 26

Characteristics of Blind Persons Attending Major Specialized Recreation Centers in New York City in 1960 37

Vision 37

Age 38

Health 39

Male and Female Members 39

Economic Level of Members 40

Education 41

Religion, Race and National Origin 41

Ability to Read Braille 42

Mobility, Outdoor and Indoor 42

Summary of Behavior Manifestations 43

Chapter *Page*

V. The Activity Program 45
Adaptations 46
Leadership and Planning 48
Arts and Crafts 49
Basketry, Raffia, Weaving, Rugmaking 51
Ceramics 54
Sculpture 59
Leather 62
Metal 62
Millinery and Sewing 64
Woodwork 66
Tiling 67
Summary 68
Dance 69
Eurythmics 70
Social Dances 73
Dramatics 76
Basic Values 76
Program Content 77
Member Selection 80
Play Selection 81
Drama Staff 82
Group Activities 84
Literary and Language Activities 87
Braille 88
Debates, Forums and Lectures 90
Languages 90
Reading Groups 90
Typing 91
Script Writing 91
Peripatology 94
Music 94
Autoharp 96
Bands 96

Chapter *Page*

Choruses ... 96
Glee Clubs and Community Sings ... 97
Guitar, Ukelele and Folk Songs ... 98
Rhythm Bands ... 99
Music Appreciation ... 99
Nature and Outings ... 101
Social Events ... 105
Sports and Games ... 106
Bingo ... 107
Bowling ... 108
Gymnastics ... 112
Pool Playing ... 113
Roller Skating ... 113
Table Games ... 114
Shuffleboard ... 119
Swimming ... 120
Miscellaneous Activities ... 124
Beauty Culture ... 125
First Aid and Home Nursing ... 125
Mobility (indoors) ... 125
Ham Radio ... 126
Religious Activities ... 126
Tape Recording Clubs ... 128
Other ... 129
VI. LEADERSHIP ... 131
Paid Staff ... 131
Leadership Qualifications ... 131
Remuneration ... 132
Volunteer Workers ... 134
Recruitment ... 135
Screening ... 136
Training ... 138
Supervision ... 139
Evaluation ... 140

Chapter *Page*

Recognition 143
Summary 143
Professions 144
VII. ADMINISTRATION 147
The Board of Directors 147
The Executive Director and Administrators 148
Supervisors 149
Employment and Personnel Practices 150
Time of Program 152
Program Season 152
Attendance 152
Daily Program Time 153
Program Planning 153
Finances 154
Records and Reports 156
Site and Facilities 158
Adaptations 159
Public Relations 162
Safety 162
Maintenance and Housekeeping 164
Evaluation 165
VIII. OPERATIONAL PRINCIPLES 167
Introduction 167
IX. SPECIALIZED PROGRAM FACTORS 181
Intake 181
Food Service and Refreshments 183
Fees for Meals 184
Dining Area 185
Transportation 185
Fees and Charges 190

Selected Bibliography 195
Index 201

RECREATION
FOR
BLIND ADULTS

Chapter I

BLINDNESS

Incidence; Prevalence; Forecast

BLINDNESS in the United States has been steadily increasing, in large measure as an associational concomitant of an aging population. In the immediate future, it is anticipated that the comparative incidence and prevalence of adventitiously blinded older adults, i.e., those sixty years and older, will soar over the current 50 per cent estimate. It is a curious paradox that although an age-old and vast literature has concerned itself with blindness as a traumatic and dramatic human impairment, accurate statistics regarding blind individuals are sadly lacking. The most widely credited estimates indicate that in 1960, there were approximately 385,000 blind persons in the United States.[1] The estimated prevalence ratio was given as 1.98 blind persons per one thousand of population, a more manageable and useful statistic. The projected total for 1970 is 400,000 blind individuals.[2] . . . However, a U. S. Public Health Service study, "Binocular Visual Acuity of Adults: United States—1960-1962," Series 11—No. 3, indicates a startling adult blind prevalence of 889,000 relative to corrected distance vision, and a figure of 1,575,000 relative to corrected near vision.

Definition

Who is considered a blind person? The terms "blind," "blindness," "legal blindness," refer to quantitative measurements of visual acuity. However, visual acuity is infinitely variable, and qualitative factors influence both perception and conception of reality. Human

[1]Ralph G. Hurlin: Estimated prevalence of blindness in the United States and in the individual states, 1960. *Sight Saving Review, XXXII,* Spring, 1962, pp. 4-12.

[2]American Foundation for the Blind, *AFB Bulletin,* No. 13, Legislation Series, April, 1959, p. 5.

perception is more than mere sensory stimuli. Perception includes extremely elaborate processes through which sensory impressions are organized into meaningful and useful concepts. Nonetheless, some objective measurements are needed to identify individuals with a degree of visual deprivation which necessitates special cultural considerations, economically, vocationally, educationally and socially. The institutional auspices of these special considerations are both public and voluntary, therefore blindness is frequently defined in law:

> The term blind person shall mean any person who has not more than 20/200 central visual acuity in the better eye with correcting lenses; or who has central visual acuity greater than 20/200 but with a limitation in the fields of vision such that the widest diameter of the visual field subtends an angle no greater than twenty degrees. Such blindness shall be certified by a physician skilled in the treatment of the human eye.[3]

When working with blind individuals, one is quickly aware that many have varying degrees of visual acuity, and that there are many levels of visual efficiency, i.e., the effective use of what is perceived. A Council on Statistics of the Blind developed a helpful chart in which visual acuity groupings related to common behavioral achievements.[4]

Laymen's Criteria	*Smellen Measurement*	*Rough Indices of Behavior*
1. Totally blind or having "light perception only."	Up to but not including 2/200.	Inability to perceive motion of hand at distance of 3 feet or less.
2. Having "motion perception" and "form perception."	Up to but not including 5/200.	Inability to count fingers at 3 feet.
3. Having "traveling sight."	Up to but not including 10/200.	Inability to read large letters such as newspaper headlines.
4. Able to read large headlines.	Up to but not including 20/200.	Inability to read 14-point or smaller type.

[3]Social Security Act, Title X, Section 1017, Definitions, Paragraph (b).

[4]Edith Kerby: *Manual on the Uses of the Standard Classification of Causes of Blindness*, prepared for the Committee on Statistics of the Blind, American Foundation for the Blind, New York, 1940, p. 23.

5. "Borderline" cases.	20/200 or more but not sufficient for an activity for which eyesight is essential.	Inability to read 10-point type or ability to read it with defect of vision so great as to be a marked handicap.

The Legally Blind with Usable Vision

Many perplexing problems in rendering services to the blind arise from the inclusion of so many "partially sighted legally blind" individuals within the eligible category. Individuals with severely impaired but with usable vision have many psychological and social problems with which they need assistance. Their problems, however, are substantively different from those faced by persons totally without sight—blind. Many blind persons bitterly resent the fact that specialized services meant for them are siphoned away by persons with limited but usable vision. Some years ago, the World Council for the Welfare of the Blind suggested a maximum sight standard for legal blindness at 10/200's with correction, instead of the current 20/200's.

It is estimated that somewhat more than half of legally blind persons do have some usable vision. Recent new advances in providing corrective glasses with low-vision lenses have enabled some legally blind persons to move from further specialized settings and services.

Of course, the factor of institutional statistics influences decisions regarding inclusion criteria which are based on degree of vision. For many agencies, quantitative achievements are dominant in appeals for community interest and support.

Meanwhile, many confusions and misunderstandings continue to be perpetuated by attributing achievements to the blind, when the performer is actually partially sighted legally blind. A blind person driving his car in city traffic, or another painting a city landscape showing minute details such as the individual bricks in a wall are examples of achievements explicable only on a miraculous and superstitious basis, if performed by totally blind individuals. Inaccurate and careless reporting of this nature results in self-doubting bitterness by those who know, especially by the totally blind who have good cause to wonder about the understanding and gullibility of the sighted. The more serious consequence is the reaffirmation and perpetuation of the traditional blindness stereotypes which continue to separate sighted individuals from blind persons. Common-sense experience about commonly expectant behavior cannot be thwarted without consequences–and by the very institutions which profess quite different educative goals.

Chapter II

HISTORICAL BACKGROUND

THE specialized recreation center for blind adults is a phenomenon of this century. All of the current centers have come into being or have had their most rapid development during and since World War II.

Specialized recreation is an integral part of the field of "service for the blind." The significance of recreation's role can be better understood within the historical perspective of the general field of blindness.

In the past, deeply influencing psychological and sociological dynamics have determined the role and status of the blind. Some of these determinants are still existent as stereotypes which continue to exorcise ghosts of expectant behaviors, for sighted persons in relation to blindness, and responsively in blind individuals themselves.

Literature about blindness is vast. Few disabilities have been the object of such early and lasting attention. There is mention of blindness in the earliest Egyptian hieroglyphics, in the early writings of the Greeks, and in the first legal codifications of the Romans.

Historically, blindness seems to have inherently offended society and to have incited fears and resentments, as if blindness were evidence of divine anger and moral judgment. Blind people were ostracized, tormented and ignored. This was a survival era.

The advent of Christianity somewhat softened the harsh rejection of maimed humanity. One of the earliest recorded expressions of official social concern for the blind was the establishment in Paris of *L'Hopital des Quinze-Vingts.* King Louis IX (St. Louis) provided this hostel for three hundred blinded Crusaders returned from battling the Saracens. In this congregate shelter, the blind busied themselves with cards and games. This was perhaps the first, dim and somewhat grim, historical recording of recreation of blind persons. However, the lot of the common blind continued to be characterized by isolation, scorn and hardship.

The English Elizabethan Poor Laws of 1601 marked an era in which, for the first time, governmental concern was expressed relative to the dependent poor, beggars, children, the ill, and the aged —but somehow, the blind were not specifically included.

In England and in France, the Renaissance period was well under way by the late seventeenth century. This was a time of extensive reasoning and speculating about the human condition. John Locks's disquisition, *Essay Concerning Human Understanding*, published in 1690, theoretically explored the question of whether, upon gaining sight, a blind person could identify an object through seeing, an object which he had learned to know only by touch. In 1709, Bishop Berkeley contributed to such deductive explorations with his *Essay Toward a New Theory of Vision.*

In 1749, Denis Diderot, who led the intellectual encyclopedists in the cataloguing of contemporary knowledge, wrote his now-famous *Essay on Blindness* (*Lettre Sur Les Aveugles*). This was the first comprehensive consideration of the mental processes of the blind and included the first recorded recommendations for specialized education. Humanitarian Rousseau called for implementation, but it was 1784 before the National Institution for the Young Blind (*L'Institution National des Jeunes Aveugles*) was founded by Valentine Haüy. This was the first formal educational institution for the blind. Like many dedicated pioneers who were to follow his example in other parts of the world, Haüy began with a single pupil. Indicative of the miserable status of the blind at the time is the fact that he had to promise to reimburse his seventeen-year-old student, Le Sueur, the amount he would lose from his begging activities while in school.

The success of *L'Institution National des Jeunes Aveugles* was soon dramatically demonstrated before learned societies and influential social groups. Similar exhibitions have continued to serve as a pattern for arousing interest and support for organized efforts to ameliorate the plight of blind persons, e.g., probably the most notable being Helen Keller in this century.

The general status of the blind in Europe and in America was, by now, a curious dichotomy of bread and circuses on the one hand, and continued rejection and isolation on the other, with the latter the more usual treatment. However, the evolutionary kettle had been stirred and placed over the fire of human wants. Long imprisoned needs for expression by blind persons had begun to simmer.

In the early nineteenth century, schools for blind children were established in Austria, England, and Germany. In 1829, Louis Braille introduced his puncto-graphic dot system for reading and writing communication. Shortly after 1830, three schools for the blind were established in the United States, under private auspices. These institutions still rank among the major specialized schools for blind children, *viz.*, Perkins Institution and Massachusetts School for the Blind, New York Institute for the Education of the Blind, and the Overbrook School for the Blind, near Philadelphia. In 1836, the first state school was started in Ohio. In 1840, Indiana enacted special legislation for the financial maintenance of the indigent blind. It was not until the end of the century that other states followed suit, Ohio in 1898, Illinois in 1903, and Wisconsin in 1907.

The economic, religious and humanistic developments in this country, just before and after the Civil War, gave rise to a philanthropic urge which led to the formation of numerous voluntary welfare groups and organizations. This was a period of fantastic economic growth with rapid industrialization and organization. While huge wealth was being created, large sections of the population were consigned to poverty and deprivation. Traditional attitudes which blamed the dependents for their plight slowly began to give way to knowledge of causative factors outside the individual. The almshouse and "bound out" practices were seen increasingly as wretched, exploitive, and inefficient. Voluntary efforts began to supplement and supplant the harsh, inadequate public welfare practices. This was to continue as the general pattern of American social welfare until the Depression of the 1930's. For blind people, the underlying and pervading attitude continued clearly enough—hostility and segregation, albeit in a more humanistic fashion. As Freud was to suggest later, one of the behavior mechanisms utilized to tolerate the intolerable is to alter its meaning; and the blind became objects to be helped, protected, and pitied.

The generation astride the turn of the century witnessed the founding of many significant social institutions and movements. This, too, was a period of reform, but in the context and ferment of industrialization, urbanization, social science and philanthropy. The settlement house, the playground movement, professional social work, the mental hygiene movement, scouting, camping, recreation were some of the sociological phenomena of the times. Helen Keller had burst upon the scene. Mark Twain referred to her as one of the wonders of the nineteenth century. Born in 1880, she still, in her eighties, is a worldwide symbol for remarkable courage and accomplishment, and a potent force in encouraging efforts and resources in behalf of blind individuals. Her oft-quoted, "Not blindness, but the attitude of the seeing to the blind is the hardest burden to bear" objectified and emphasized the extrinsic sociological effects of blindness.

Education for the blind was accepted and expected. Now, it was important to find work for them, keep them busy; and a wave of establishing employment institutions for the blind spread over the country. The blind quickly demonstrated that they could be productive with their hands, i.e., make brooms, mops, mattresses, baskets. Then, by combining manual dexterity with hearing capacity, they could tune pianos and transcribe recorded materials. Vending stands and small business enterprises were a favorite field for those who possessed some business ability. Many major voluntary philanthropic organizations for the blind had their origins during this period, *viz.*, The Industrial Home for the Blind, in 1893; The New York Association for the Blind, in 1905; The Chicago Lighthouse for the Blind, in 1906; The National Society for the Prevention of Blindness, in 1908; The Braille Institute of America, in 1919; The American Foundation for the Blind, in 1921, and many others.

Technological developments and mass production methods were unmitigated blessings for blind people. The radio, typewriter, telephone, phonograph and tape machine enormously enlarged communication links with the sighted. Assembly units, transcribing machines and a host of inventions and electronic gadgets increased the blind person's economic usefulness and social stature—and around the corner was World War II which would demand the utmost in production from all citizens, including the handicapped.

Just prior to this period, the Depression of the 1930's had required a fundamental alteration of American social and political philosophy. The federal government became an active participant in public welfare and a new American value came into prominence, i.e., social security. When relief measures were organized and made permanent in 1935, Title X of the Social Security Act contained special provisions for assistance to indigent blind persons. In 1936, the Randolph-Sheppard Act permitted licensed blind individuals to operate vending stands in federal buildings, greatly stimulating such employment for the blind.

In 1938, the Wagner-O'Day Act created a committee of government officials to be concerned with the quality, quantity and price of blind-made products to be purchased by various departments of the federal government. An Agency known as National Industries for the Blind was designated to facilitate the distribution of government orders among the agencies for the blind. These orders became the mainstay of most sheltered workshops which employ thousands of blind persons.

During World War II, thousands of additional blind workers came into their own, occupationally and economically. Consonant with the end of the war, the Bardin-La Follette Act of 1945 established an extensive federal-state cooperative structure for the vocational rehabilitation of all blind adults who could be brought to any level of productive capacity. At the same time, social science findings were being implemented through sophisticated disciplines in which individualization and human dignity were dominant articles of faith. Integration of human differences was becoming a groundswell beckoning all to emerge into a new wonderful era of substantive human values and appreciations. It appeared that, at long last, blind persons would emerge as full-fledged members of their community—and many did.

It has been justly stated that there has been more progress in work for the blind in the past fifty years than in all the preceding thousands. But somehow, just below the surface of progress, old conflicts and fears still lurk.

Novelist Ishbel Ross in a generalized study of the problem perceptively stated:

> The blind are still the blind—dependent on countless small services that niggle at their self-respect, confronted by innumerable daily frustrations. It takes the most vigorous and strongest to strike out for effort rather than ease. For one who breasts the current, hundreds give up.[1]

From data gleaned in a more definitive study, sociologist Joseph S. Himes, Jr. reported:

> The evidence leaves little doubt that popular attitudes toward the blind are changing. . . . Perhaps the most we dare conclude is that the changes noted comprise no more than a few random and inchoate tendencies, a bright spot the size of a man's hand against the dark horizon of ancient and foreboding prejudices.[2]

The human sciences are enlarging and deepening their inquiries into the phenomenon of blindness. Its complex nature is enshrouded not only in the matrix of sociological dynamics but also deep in the psyche of all individuals. The American Foundation for the Blind, Inc., the foremost research organization in the field, is encouraging systematic explorations which will shed the light of reality on the factors which tend to separate the sighted from the blind and vice versa.

Meanwhile, and probably for a long time in the future, the specialized recreation center for blind adults will continue to be a needed and wanted community facility. Whether justified in terms of special service to meet special needs, or because emotional barriers obscure the understanding of those responsible for community service, the fact remains that in the specialized recreation centers many blind adults experience fertile and provocative forms of recreation which meet their needs. This is the implicit philosophical underpinning of individuality which leads to dignity for the individual who is blind.

In the specialized center milieu, understanding and acceptance can be promoted through sharing the genuine satisfactions and enjoyments afforded through recreation. Here, all participants tend to be more genuine, disarming and disarmed. Here, disturbing

[1] Ishbel Ross: *Journey Into Light.* New York, Appleton-Century-Crofts, Inc., 1951, pp. 6-7.

[2] Joseph S. Himes, Jr.: Changing attitudes of the public toward the blind, *The New Outlook for the Blind*, LII, No. 9, November, 1958, p. 335.

mannerisms of blind persons can be differentiated, individualized and experienced as exterior and superficial elements of a character which on the whole may be informed, competent, humorous, and altogether delightful and admirable. Here, a warmth of friendship can promote mutual understanding and respect based on the more essential aspects of personality.

Recreation Programs for Blind Adults

Organized specialized recreation for blind adults is of relatively recent origin. The muck-raking era of social reform, early in the twentieth century, provided the setting for elite charity-minded volunteers to express their humanitarian concern for the blind by providing a facility in which their hardships could be temporarily ameliorated. The recreation service developed together with, and sometimes even before, other services for blind persons, e.g., medical, financial, adjustment, vocational training, and employment. There was early realization that one of the hardest of human experiences was to find oneself without resources to fill unoccupied time.

The three oldest and largest agencies for the blind in the United States are located in New York City, *viz.*, The Industrial Home for the Blind, known as the I.H.B., founded in 1893; The New York Association for the Blind, known as the Lighthouse, founded in 1905, and the New York Jewish Guild for the Blind, usually referred to as The Guild, founded in 1914. The original formal expression of I.H.B. purposes was to furnish a home for blind men; to provide suitable employment, such as chair caning, mattress making and repairing, and to provide recreation, rest, and congenial association.[3] The Lighthouse began as a ticket service to provide blind persons with donated unused theatre and concert tickets.[4] Two years later, the Lighthouse was a multi-service agency for the blind. The first Guild purposes included: (1) friendly meeting; (2) direct relief; (3) the institutionalization of children; (4) the institutionalization of older adult Jewish blind, and (5) the establishment of a recreation center.[5]

[3]Industrial Home for the Blind: *The I.H.B. Way: An Approach to the Rehabilitation of Blind Persons.* Brooklyn, N. Y., 1961, p. 4.

[4]The New York Association for the Blind: *op. cit.*, p. 9.

[5]New York Guild for the Jewish Blind: *Staff Manual.* New York, 1962, p. 1

It would be unrealistic to deny that some defensive motivational factors provided the energy and grist for these philanthropic endeavors. In historical perspective, one is constrained not to think in terms of "bread and circuses," nor of the need to assuage fear, hostility and guilt caused by the mere fact of "their" observable presence. It would be shamefully unrealistic to disregard the positive idealism with which these reformers plunged into a centuries-old area of human deprivation. To inquire too closely into the motivations of these apparently sincere and humanitarian volunteers who freely gave of their energy, time and other resources is perhaps like "looking a gift horse in the mouth." The history of social welfare is replete with such leaders who helped us to move along the evolutionary path from political to social democracy in which, ideally, the concern of all the people may become the organized concern of all the people.

In a democratic society which was becoming more aware of and more concerned about the individual, it was not possible to continue to ignore the plight of large numbers of adults for whom blindness was a consignment to the isolation and uselessness of the past. "Helping the blind to help themselves" and "Light through work" became rallying slogans through which at least some blind adults began to move into the stream of productive life.

In the early recreation programs, the core activity was the gathering together to be joyous, to exchange accounts of achievements and/or hardships, to be entertained, and to partake of refreshments. The centers had a desultory existence. Their degree of activity was determined largely by the capacity of the particular individual in charge of the program.

Shortly after World War II, two professional disciplines, Recreation and Social Work, had a significant impact upon the purposes, objectives, and practices of the specialized recreation centers.

Chapter III

RECREATION AND SOCIAL GROUP WORK

The desire of mankind to find pleasure and satisfaction, in hours free from toil, is as old as man himself. So fundamental and universal is the human need for recreation that the reference to recreation as a teleological phenomenon is appropriate. Under many guises, determined by cultural circumstances, the human need for diversionary and creative experiences seems to be as inherent in the species of man as the need to communicate.

In a democratic society, social institutions are a function of individual and community needs, and derive their sanction and validity from the commitment to serve these needs. Human beings must be active, develop and use all their capacities. We are beginning to understand more fully that boredom and purposelessness can cripple and kill, slowly and insidiously, but just as mercilessly as a bullet or an exposure to radiation. Inactive and isolated, the individual deteriorates, sickens and becomes a liability to himself and to his community.

Professional Recreation

In the vocabulary of the average American citizen, recreation is a common word usually associated with any enjoyable non-remunerative activity. This understanding is similar to the definition used by many professional recreators, i.e., recreation is activity, voluntarily engaged in during leisure and motivated by the personal satisfactions which result from it. Recreation is behavior, mental and/or physical, which is an expression of human needs and desires. Recreation has also been defined as a consummative experience, non-debilitating in nature, which in the most literal sense is a re-creation of the individual. In our modern urbanized and specialized lives, the notion of individual re-creation, and wholeness implied by consummative experience, are significant for the health of all persons, including those without vision. It is now widely accepted that recreation is an essential part of every person's life; and, in a general sense, recreation may be thought of as a fundamental need of man.[1]

Basic Human Needs: Basic Recreation Needs

What is a basic human need? So fundamental a concept requires a comprehensive and learned definition. Harvard psychologist H. A. Murray has stated that

> a need is a construct (a convenient fiction or hypothetical concept) which stands for a force (the physio-chemical nature is unknown) in the brain, a force which organizes perception, apperception, intellection, conation, and action in such a way as to transform in a certain direction an existing unsatisfactory situation.[2]

Standard dictionaries succinctly synthesize these ingredients of human need into exigencies or conditions requiring supply or relief. Basic human needs refer to "these needs which everyone has, regardless of age, sex or station in life, such as a sense of personal worth, status recognition, love, a sense of belonging, and attainment of some measure of one's efforts, as well as physical requirements."[3] Sociological and anthropological findings support the notion that a universal biological restlessness or tension becomes a "need" requiring supply or relief, and that at the level of consciousness, this need becomes socially shaped and defined, i.e., a derived need.

Academic, experimental, and functional psychologists tend to distinguish two major groupings of basic human needs, *viz.*, (1) needs which are primarily physiological in nature, qualitatively innate in the species, and functionally concerned with organic survival, e.g., inspiration and expiration, food and defecation, water and urination, passivity, sex, etc., and (2) needs which are derived

[1]Jay B. Nash, *Philosophy of Recreation and Leisure*. St. Louis: C. V. Mosby Company, 1953, p. 208.

[2]H. A. Murray, *Explorations in Personality*. New York; Oxford University Press, 1938, p. 123.

[3]Carter V. Good (ed.): *Dictionary of Education*. 2nd ed., New York, McGraw-Hill Book Company, Inc., 1959, p. 362.

from the group in interaction with the psychological nature of man. These secondary needs are termed psychogenic needs.

Social scientists acknowledge the tenuous validity of trying to atomize and identify discrete psychological needs. Holistic man is infinitely complex and variable in his dynamic experiences. His inner and outer environments ceaselessly interact to determine the quality and quantity of his living. Psychologist Murray expressed this notion as follows: "A human being is a motile, discriminating, valuating, assimilating, adapting, integrating, differentiating and reproducing temporal unity within a changing environmental matrix."[4] Nonetheless, many authoritative psychologists have, through various scientific methodologies, identified discrete psychogenic needs. In turn, well-known recreation-educators have analyzed recreation activities in relation to these identified basic human needs.

Despite semantic peregrinations, content analysis of authoritative recreation literature reveals a high correlation between basic human needs and needs met through recreation activities. An analysis of ten standard college textbooks used in graduate courses in recreation produced a list of identified basic human needs developed in psychology. Table I shows the many psychogenic needs met through organized recreation activities and experiences. These findings emphasize the predominance of man's social nature as indicated by the full scores accorded to the need for achievement, recognition, and exhibition.

TABLE I

PSYCHOGENIC-RECREATION NEEDS

A–Nash; B–Hunt; C–Danford; D–Slavsen; E–Athletic Institute; F–Robbins; G–Butler; H–Trecker; I–Meyer and Brightbill; J–Stafford

	A	B	C	D	E	F	G	H	I	J	Total
Category I											
Acquisition	X				X	X			X		4
Conseverence	X										1
Order											0
Retention											0
Construction	X	X	X	X	X		X	X	X	X	9
Category II											
Achivement	X	X	X	X	X	X	X	X	X	X	10

[4]Murray, *op. cit.*, p. 36.

Recognition	X	X	X	X	X	X	X	X	X	X	10
Exhibition	X	X	X	X	X	X	X	X	X	X	10
Category III											
Inviolacy		X		X		X					3
Seclusion		X									1
Infravoidance		X									1
Dependence	X	X									2
Counteraction	X	X	X								3

TABLE I–*Continued*

A–Nash; B–Hunt; C–Danford; D–Slavsen; E–Athletic Institute; F–Robbins; G–Butler; H–Trecker; I–Meyer and Brightbill; J–Stafford

	A	B	C	D	E	F	G	H	I	J	Total
Category IV											
Dominance	X		X	X	X	X					5
Deference	X	X	X	X	X						5
Simulance	X	X	X	X	X	X	X	X			8
Autonomy	X	X	X								3
Contrariness	X	X	X								3
Category V											
Aggression	X	X	X	X		X					5
Abasement	X		X	X							3
Category VI											
Blame avoidance	X			X							2
Category VII											
Affiliation	X	X	X	X	X	X	X	X	X	X	10
Rejection	X										1
Nurturance	X	X	X		X		X				5
Succorance	X		X	X	X						4
Play	X	X	X	X	X	X		X		X	8
Category VIII											
Cognizance	X	X	X	X	X	X	X		X	X	9
Exposition	X	X	X		X	X	X		X	X	8
Category IX											
Sexuality		X	X	X	X		X				5
Activity	X	X	X	X	X	X	X	X			8
Creativity	X	X				X		X	X	X	6
Aesthetic	X	X			X	X	X				5
Totals	26	23	20	17	17	15	12	9	9	9	157

The horizontal capitalized letters in Table I refer to prominent authoritative writers and educators in professional recreation. The first eight categories of psychogenic needs, listed vertically, were derived by psychologist Murray in his experiments which led to the development of the widely known Thematic Apperception Test (T.A.T.). The ninth miscellaneous category was added because the specific needs therein were identified as recreation needs by at least half of the ten authorities.

Professor Murray's eight categories were delineated on the basis of the factors which follow:

Category I. Needs associated with inanimate objects; sometimes with animals, i.e., acquiring friends, maintaining loyalties, possessiveness, organizing groups.

Category II. Needs commonly called ambition, will-to-power, desire for accomplishment and prestige.

Category III. Complementary to achievement and recognition are the desires and actions which involve the defense of status or the avoidance of humiliation.

Category IV. Needs which have to do with humanpower exerted, resisted or yielded to.

Category V. Needs (dichotomous) sado-masochistic.

Category VI. Need to restrain primitive, asocial impulses in order to remain an accepted member of the culture.

Category VII. Needs which have to do with affection between people, seeking it, exchanging it, giving it, withholding it.

Category VIII. Need to ask and tell.

Transition from the concept of basic human needs to the concept of basic recreation needs is hardly obtuse. Many eminent recreation authorities utilize the "recreation needs" concept. George D. Butler, consultant of the National Recreation Association, declares that "a characteristic of all forms of recreation is that each provides an outlet for some basic urge or need."[5] Jay B. Nash, a dean of modern recreation-educators, refers to recreation as a complement to work and a need for all men.[6]

Whether defined as a kind of experience, a professional field of work, or an integral part of living, recreation always involves human behavior and human experience which is expressive of and responsive to individual needs. The range and variety of recreation pursuits which gives to people the opportunities for gratifying

[5]George D. Butler: *Introduction to Community Recreation.* 2nd ed., New York, McGraw-Hill Book Company, Inc., 1947, p. 207.

[6]Nash, *op. cit.*, p. 208.

expressions is almost limitless. Through extensive experience and study, professional recreators have delineated and classified specific areas of recreation endeavors. The comprehensive identification of recreation activity areas has enabled program planners and administrators to include a cafeteria of activities to meet the wide variety of needs, interests, capabilities and capacities of people. Individual personality is expressed through the exercise of physical, social, mental and creative needs. Recreation activities and experiences, in varied forms, bring physical, social, mental and creative satisfactions to the individual.

The impact of organized recreation on the established recreation programs for blind persons was considerable. For the first time, the explicit philosophy and principles of a professional discipline gave direction to the program. Leadership improved. Facilities, equipment, and activities were expanded. Attitudes toward members as well as attitudes of the members toward themselves began to slowly change. Individualized program planning and small group activities began to supplant large non-participation events. Programs began to be designed to meet most effectively the needs, interests and capacities of the members. Independence, mobility and activity became dominant objectives. Recreation was recognized as an important adjunct service in rehabilitation.

After many years of procrastination and delay, the American Association of Workers for the Blind gave recognition to these developments by permitting the organization of a national Recreation Committee. At the 1955 annual convention of the A.A.W.B. in Quebec, Canada, three papers were read, all of which were concerned with specialized recreation center programs.[7]

It was into this setting that another professional discipline was introduced to give even more qualitative substance to the recreation service.

Social Group Work

Social group work is a method in the profession of social work; an orderly, systematic, planned way of working with people in groups. Social group work is a method through which individuals

[7]American Association of Workers for the Blind, Inc.; *Proceedings*, June, 1955, pp. 164-173.

in groups are helped by a worker who guides their interaction in program activities so that they may relate themselves to others and experience growth opportunities in accordance with their needs and capacities. In social group work, the group itself is utilized by the individual, with the help of the worker, as a primary means of personality growth, change and development.[8]

Specialized recreation center participants are particularly amenable to social group work methodology because of the frequent observation that people who find social relationships difficult can sometimes understand and help each other when they are brought together in groups. In these designed groups, relationships can be guided and performance and achievement made positive so that a sense of accomplishment results. This is particularly important because blind persons so often experience the "frustration of mastery" in the non-specialized setting.

Group workers can planfully structure individual programs so that most included activities will tend to be ego-supportive. The trained worker is sensitively aware that even simple failure can exact a heavy price for handicapped individuals who keenly feel their loss of orientation and control of the environment. Therefore, failures are anticipated and minimized.

The group worker understands that a blinded person tends to lose his social identity. His ego is weakened just when it needs to be strongest. To the qualified worker, it is a common diagnostic observation that in order to preserve identity, blind individuals may try to withdraw and exclude all stimuli, thus protecting the boundaries of their weakened egos. They sit rigid or quietly rocking, hearing only what they wish to hear, as if to conserve energy to avoid impending challenges. Such repressive behavior may be followed by helpless attempts to do, in order to coerce love, while, at the same time, bemoaning the necessity to be so dependent. These mechanisms of behavior are familiar to the social group worker who appropriately protects, supports, enables, teaches and guides the reorganizing member toward some resocialization.

Social work knowledge and values enable the group worker to recognize the reality of the limitations which society imposes

[8]Harleigh B. Trecker; *Social Group Work Principles and Practices.* New York, Whiteside, Inc., 1955, p. 5.

upon the role functioning of blind persons, and the fact that such role deprivation presents problems which no amount of supportive or restorative work can deny. Thus, the group worker understands the mixture of aggressive, withdrawal, compliant, and dependent behavior frequently encountered in groups in which blind persons share their ascribed status which all too quickly modifies their particular needs.

However, a group, *per se*, may not necessarily be constructive. A trained leader is essential to direct the group in the give-and-take interpersonal relationships of the members with each other and with the leader. The group leader must be planful and purposeful, so that interactions are directed in a manner which will enable the members to constructively meet their needs.

Regrettably, considerable unprofessional feelings have been engendered between recreators and social group workers. Professional inferiority has been imputed to the recreation worker who may not always be a qualified and/or certified professional, and who often tends to be preoccupied with activities to keep participants active and happy. The group worker usually has a master's degree in social work, although the title "group worker" is also variously used.

Some group workers believe that work with blind persons is so highly specialized that social group work should be the only methodology employed in the specialized centers. The implicit assumption that social group workers possess many common recreation and teaching skills is not substantiated by experiences in many specialized recreation centers—and social group workers also become pre-occupied with individualistic activities for the members. It is important to remember that all professional intervention is goal-directed toward objectives determined as helpful rather than hurtful, regardless of whether the worker is engaged in recreation or social group work. The capacity to be a person, to have opinions, to contradict, to make suggestions and to function alone and/or to participate with others can be strengthened in many ways, as long as the methods used do not obscure and negate the objectives.

The roots of living and doing lie not in theories and conceptions but rather in conduct and in experience. Basic human needs can be identified and their satisfactions generalized. However, without taking into account the screen of values which gives style and capacity to each personality, the worker literally blinds himself to reality—and no professional identification can protect him from continuous ineffectiveness.

Common Elements in Recreation and Social Group Work

Both professions express identical preventive and therapeutic concerns and objectives for the same universe of blind participants and their communities. Both professions are knowledgeable about basic human needs, the significance of their satisfactions, and the effects of blindness upon these needs as well as upon the opportunities for their satisfaction. Recreators and social group workers both understand that blindness does not standardize behavior, yet may alter a particular individual's methods and sources for the satisfaction of his needs. Workers in both professions utilize similar facilities, equipment and materials to achieve similar objectives founded in identical professional philosophies.

The prominent operating principles contained in Chapter VIII were distilled and crystallized from both recreation and social group work practices and experiences. Conjointly and cooperatively, recreation and social group work can continue to provide the knowledge, skills and practices which make organized specialized recreation programs necessary adjuncts for effecting personal, social and vocational rehabilitation, as well as habilitation for the significantly large number of blind persons for whom adequate restoration to former status and activity cannot realistically be achieved.

Chapter IV

THE IMPACT OF BLINDNESS

VISUAL impairment, like other serious physical handicaps, has significant multiple effects upon many basic human needs and, reciprocally, upon opportunities and means for their satisfactions. General self-doubt and denigration of ego are frequently observed resultants of blindness. Ego is here conceived as the executive and control factors of the psyche—those aspects of thought and feeling processes in which experiences are evaluated and behavior results. Ego is functionally the core of personality, even more so in cultures which traditionally place high worth on individualism, independence, free will and personal responsibility. Manner and degree of adaptation to crises and stresses are largely determined by ego-strengths and/or ego-weaknesses, as an individual struggles to survive the realities of his situation as only he experiences them.

Every person is a biochemical, psychosocial, philosophical matrix of elements and forces which ceaselessly interact in the inner and outer, animate and inanimate, environments of the individual. Homeostatic and ecological balances noted in human physiology and in nature suggest mutually sensitive interrelationships between and among an individual's physical, mental and emotional states. Changes in one state affect the others. Behavior is therefore the expression of a person's unique needs at a particular physiological, psychosocial and psychic phase of development.

Physique has tangible properties, real and actual, which are appropriate or inappropriate for necessary accomplishments, roles and statuses. Physical vision is generally considered to be "the Queen of the senses." The world is largely structured for and dominated by visual stimuli. There is widespread agreement that blindness limits and restricts impressions, expressions, communications, orientations and consequent interactions which help to determine self-identification and self-worth.

In the vast literature of blindness, few investigators, except for some auto-inspirational biographers, have noted any positive resultants of blindness. In one of the first competent systematic studies, French suggested two possible compensatory effects of blindness:

> . . . the first, in what may be termed survivals of the more primitive senses, recalling in some respects the sense life of lower organisms; the second, in an increased attentiveness to the data of the remaining senses, causing their seeming poverty to give place to a certain riches through attention to their immediate impressions, but even more through new interpretations which are partly the result of experience.[1]

Blind persons are inevitably faced with a continual series of adaptive crises in which immobilizing anxieties and tensions are frequent—even after they have been helped to develop more adequate and positive responses to the demands of their needs. Nevertheless, careful diagnostic observations of how blind persons meet their physiological needs for activity and passivity, their psychosocial needs for ego-development and human relationships, and their spiritual needs for subjective purposeful being, clearly indicate that visual impairments do not specifically standardize resultant behavior.

Visual perception in humans is neither a single nor a simple phenomenon. It is a set of extremely elaborate processes through which sensory impressions are organized into meaningful and useful concepts of objects and events which happen around us and inside us. Visual efficiency, or lack of it, is easily discernible in individuals. Improvement in awareness and in effective usefulness of what is visually perceived is common experience in many professions where effectiveness in observation is vital. The same is true for the other major senses: hearing, touch, smell and taste.

Recently, astonishing evidence of a new hidden sense, "dermo-optical perception," (D.O.P.), has been widely reported as a result

[1]Richard Slayton French: *From Homer to Helen Keller: A Social and Educative Study of the Blind*. New York, American Foundation for the Blind, Inc., 1932, p. 12.

of psychological experiments in the Soviet Union. Apparently, some individuals possess an innate ability to reliably perceive color differentiations through the skin of the finger-tips, elbows, foreheads and other parts of the body. Allegedly, the talent can be trained. D O P has been greeted with hopeful excitement and skeptical disdain. The validated existence of dermal perception will unquestionably be a great boon to some blind persons who have this "new" sense.

However useful color differentiation and perhaps even reading of regular print may be, reference to this trait as a type of vision seems more journalistic than practical, and likely to encourage disappointing expectations in blind and sighted persons. As a matter of fact, indications of a type of dermal sensitivity were hypothesized and noted when obstacle-perception was investigated and later found to be primarily an aural phenomenon. Nevertheless, the new findings seem to emphasize anew the significance of discovering, training and utilizing all the senses which a blind person may possess so that as far as possible, he can function efficiently and independently without vision, the "Queen of the senses."

Intrinsic and Extrinsic Effects of Blindness

Visual impairment has significant effects upon basic human needs, upon opportunities for their satisfaction, and upon the manner of their expression. Behavioral scientists researching the effects of blindness have grouped the resultants into two general and interrelated categories, *viz.*, (1) intrinsic effects which derive essentially from inner deprivations like decreased sensory stimulations and consequent restricted mental and physical activity; and (2) extrinsic effects which derive from the social milieu in which expectant behavior is stereotyped as dependent and inferior—which all too soon becomes the self-image of the handicapped individual.

Physiological findings indicate that human organisms require a certain rate of sensory impact in order to maintain the functioning of the perceptual apparatus. Recent sociological studies intimate that since modern urban man develops primarily as a social being, extrinsic effects are the more dominating and controlling in determining the status and behavior of blind persons through the manner and provision of activities which supposedly meet their basic human needs.

Discrete intrinsic and extrinsic effects of blindness have been identified and delineated by some authoritative social scientists. Early in 1932, the American Foundation for the Blind published French's *From Homer to Helen Keller: A Social and Educative Study of the Blind*. Limitations resulting from blindness were developed as follows:

1. Great impoverishment in the life of sense impressions.
2. Almost complete loss of the power of physical orientation.
3. Physical and mental timidity, sedentary habits, excessive introspection and the substitution of verbal symbols for concrete reality.
4. Lowered physical and mental vitality.
5. Nervousness and nervous habits, blindisms.
6. Social inadequacy due to attitudes of the sighted toward blindness, and fostered by the stigmata accompanying blindness, i.e., rolling eyes, bulging eyeballs, disfigured eyes.[2]

At about the same time in 1932, a psychologist, whose analytical and systematic findings were more impressive because he was himself totally blind, concluded, "Blindness is not the mere absence or impairment of a single sense. The human organism functions as a dynamic whole and blindness changes and completely reorganizes the mental life of an individual."[3]

In 1938, Harvard psychologist Hayes confirmed seventeenth and eighteenth century speculative and theoretical deductions to the effect that sensory compensations resulting from blindness were non-existent.[4]

Setting the stage for a more comprehensive delineation of the effects of blindness, educator Berthold Lowenfeld suggested three general areas in which visual deprivation restricted an individual, *viz.*, (1) in the range and variety of concepts; (2) in the ability to

[2]French, *op. cit.*, p. 26.

[3]Thomas D. Cutsforth: *The Blind in School and Society*. New York, American Foundation for the Blind, 1951 edition, p. 2.

[4]Samuel P. Hayes: The psychology of blindness, *What of the Blind*, ed., Helga Lende. New York, American Foundation for the Blind, 1938, pp. 88-101.

get about, and (3) in the control of the environment.[5]

After World War II, psychiatric and psychoanalytical concepts began to permeate findings about the effects of blindness. Illustrative of this new tack we read "Most psychiatrists of the modern school would unhesitatingly interpret the data concerning the feelings entertained down through the ages toward the blind as evidence of the mobilization of a castration complex arrived at emotionally by the displacement of the eyes to the sex organs."[6] Alleging that independence in movement was the prime problem of the blind person, perhaps because one of the authors, Chevigny, seemed to be so inordinately proud of his own guide dog, the book went on to specify eight concomitants of blindness which were essentially extrinsic effects:

1. The blind tended to be surrounded with wonder and awe.
2. Conflict was engendered because reorganization was expected to take place in accord with acceptable standards for the sighted.
3. The notion that loss of sight meant loss of intellect.
4. The notion that blind persons dwelled in darkness.
5. Mentally, the blind had a void which was a direct result of lack of sight.
6. Physically, there was little or nothing a blind person could do.
7. Blind persons were emotionally deprived and sad.
8. Blind persons were proven sinners.[7]

More academically, Professor of Psychology, Worchel, advised that "factors like age of onset, progression and degrees of blindness, efficiency in relation to tasks, intelligence, sex, education, parental attitudes, family composition, cultural factors, etc., precluded the consideration of blindness as a single and measurable variable. "Blindness was seen as a deviation from the normal, but not as a unique kind of psychology." Based primarily on the technique of extrapolation, there were at least five major areas of human be-

[5]Berthold Lowenfeld: Psychological principles in home teaching, *Outlook for the Blind and the Teachers Forum.* XXXVIII, No. 2, February, 1944, pp. 31-35.

[6]Hector Chevigny and Sydell Braverman: *The Adjustment of the Blind.* New Haven, Yale University Press, 1950, p. 64.

[7]Chevigny and Braverman, *ibid., pp.* 1-71.

havior in which limitations could be expected to occur as a result of blindness:

1. Personality adjustment characterized by feelings of helplessness and resulting in overcompensation and social withdrawal with excessive phantasy manifestations.
2. Mobility restrictions in relation to the special environment resulting in physical fear of pain when in an unknown area.
3. Space perception in relation to general and specific orientation.
4. Communication, verbal and non-verbal.
5. Creativity.[8]

An authentic social science survey of systematic investigations into the effects of blindness led to these conclusions:

1. The incidence of the visually disabled appears to be increasing in the United States.
2. Attitudes toward blindness as a condition are uniformly negative.
3. Public attitudes toward blind persons are not unfavorable, but covert attitudes are often perceived by the blind as hostile and derogatory.
4. Parents of blind children and persons who work with the blind not infrequently exhibit contradictory behavior resulting from a conflict in attitudes.
5. On personality inventories, the blind more frequently than the seeing earn scores that fall in the "maladjusted" range. The possibility that this is an artifact of the standardization procedures has not been eliminated.
6. The evidence is clear that the social maturity of the blind child is retarded when measured on a scale designed for seeing children.
7. Mild visual impairments, except perhaps the traumatic loss of one eye, are probably not crucial for behavior.
8. Severe visual disability is not associated with severe personality disturbance in the overwhelming proportion of persons studied. Personality characteristics existing before incurring a visual disability appear to be important.
9. The presence of substantial differences among the visually

[8]Philip Worchel: Psychological implications of blindness, *The Seer*, The Pennsylvania Association for the Blind), *xxiv*, No. 3, September, 1954, p. 30.

handicapped has been confirmed. It has been demonstrated that many personality and adjustment patterns are possible for different individuals who have the same degree of defective vision.

10. Much of the evidence from research must be interpreted cautiously, and some of it must be rejected because of serious methodological inadequacies. These inadequacies are not inherent in research on problems of visual impairment, although many of them are not easy to remedy.[9]

An encompassing point of view of the effects of blindness on the individual was expressed by psychiatrist Cholden, one of the few psycho-therapists to have direct comprehensive experience working with blind persons. "The adult who loses his sight faces a task that can be succinctly stated as one of internal reorganization to the fact that he is now a different person. His capacities, his interests, his social position, his body image, his aspirations are all affected, if not completely changed."[10]

Unfortunately, Dr. Cholden's untimely death, shortly after the publication of his findings, ended his interesting depth exploration into the effects of blindness.

In reviewing the literature on the effects of blindness, one becomes aware of a curious difference in emphasis in the identification and delineation of restrictions which result. Sighted investigators like French, Lowenfeld, Worchel and Cholden seem to give more predominant attention to the intrinsic effects of blindness. Extrinsic effects get more attention when the investigators are themselves blind, e.g., Cutsforth, Chevigny, Himes and Gowman.

In 1950, Sociologist Joseph S. Himes, Jr., who is visually handicapped, presented a definitive analysis of the sociological mechanisms which (1) interpreted the meaning of blindness and the personality of the blind; (2) defined the standard social situations, and (3) controlled social behavior, thus making it orderly and predictable.[11]

[9]Roger G. Barker, *et al.*: *Adjustment to Physical Handicap and Illness: A Survey of the Social Psychology of Physique and Disability*. New York, Social Science Research Council, Bulletin 55, Revised, 1953, p. 289.

[10]Louis S. Cholden: *A Psychiatrist Works with Blindness*. New York, American Foundation for the Blind, Inc., 1958, p. 73.

[11]Joseph S. Himes, Jr.: Some concepts of blindness in American culture, *Social Casework, XXXI,* No. 10, December, 1950, pp. 410-416.

Himes described the three major factors which determined the social adjustment of physically handicapped persons in our society:

1. The character and extent of the specific disability as these restricted and impeded ability to behave according to normal expectations in particular places and situations.
2. The socially and culturally defined reactions to the disability. These were classified into two crystallized group reactions:
   (a) The more desirable and more objective admission of reality behavior limitations which allowed for necessary adjustments, but which regarded the disabled person as capable of normal social behavior in areas not directly affected by the physical impairment.
   (b) The less desirable and more subjective combining of fact and fancy into a social stereotype which saw the handicapping character of the disability diffused throughout the total personality and the behavior system. Three fairly consistent cultural constructs relative to the stereotyped view of blindness were presented, as follows:

   (1) The blind beggar, characterized by shuffling, timid feet, guided by the staccato tapping of the metal tip of a white cane; a spasmodically moving tin cup with the thin metallic sound of a few symbolic coins; dark glasses, musical instruments like accordion, banjo or guitar; and shabby clothing. The picture is one of a cautious, timid, defeated individual, who had the cards stacked against him and who had retired from the struggle to a life of useless dependency. Frequently, the picture implied that the blind beggar was both stupid and ignorant, incapable of socially useful activity.
   (2) The "blind genius" was characterized by almost complete absence of the beggary symbols, and was possessed of extraordinary talents and uniqueness of personality, which was demonstrated by average or superior performance in areas presumed to be impossible for blind persons, i.e., a superior college student, a talented musician, a successful lawyer, college professor or judge.
   (3) The notion that loss of vision was organically compensated by increased acuteness of the other major senses, was

still a widespread, almost superstitious belief, despite the known, theoretical, empirical and experimental data to the contrary.[12]

In 1957, social scientist Alan Gowman, blinded veteran, contributed a book, *The War Blind in American Social Structure*, in which the stronger emphasis was on extrinsic effects. Said Gowman, "The psychology of the blind is the psychology of isolation," and "It is bad enough to be shut in; it is far worse to be shut out."[13]

The contents of Dr. Gowman's book were derived from his doctoral study and dissertation at Harvard University. Noting that every human status had its own set of deprivations and compensations, Gowman analyzed the specific losses resulting from blindness as follows:

A. *Contraction of the experiential field*:

1. Visual perceptions and attendant conceptions were seriously cut off.
2. Lessened orientation.
3. Lessened appreciation of many phases of life.
4. Lessened and altered intuition at most elementary levels because of absence of visual contact.
5. Curtailed opportunities for recreation in a leisure-centered society.
6. Curtailed reading because auditory and braille materials were less extensive and comprehensive; no skim reading of newspapers and magazines which form the light conversations of casual interactions.
7. Lessened intellectual stimulation and growth.
8. Diluted and foreshortened individual responses to base stimuli which stem from a combination of perceptual and conceptual cues as these relate to sex, food and beauty values.
9. Experience must be constructed of fewer building blocks.
10. Lessening of the potentials for combinations and permutations of stimuli because stimulations must take more narrowly channeled forms.
11. Inhibited creativity and compression of the natural fullness

[12] *Ibid.*, p. 412.

[13] Alan G. Gowman: *The War Blind in American Social Structure*. New York, American Foundation for the Blind, Inc., 1957, p. XV.

of the real world because of impoverished perceptual experiences.

12. Lessened maturity of ideas and images because of lack of shading and roundness of experience.
13. Fewer guide-posts so that blind individuals missed many events on the most prosaic level, i.e., billboards, signs, silhouettes.
14. Fewer alternative choices of behavior because the range of action was collapsed.
15. The confining environment tended to invade areas other than just that of sensory experience.

The preceding fifteen restrictions resulting from blindness are obviously not mutually exclusive, and they are primarily intrinsic in content. In the next group, of nine limitations, Gowman begins the movement into extrinsic and more social areas.

B. *Ambiguities and devaluation of status*:

1. Lessened economic sufficiency with blind persons generally viewed as public charges. Sensory limitations drastically limited job opportunities, and even tasks not requiring vision were geared to visual cues.
2. Stereotyped social roles and statuses in which blindness was the first criterion of description.
3. Equating of blindness with incompetence so that even ordinary achievements were greeted with amazement rather than with a realistic appraisal of performance.
4. The status of the blind person was always special, connoting strangeness.
5. Segregation because of exclusions from occupational and recreational systems, and the conversational shifts when a blind person joins a group.
6. Full status in our country was vested in part upon an individual's possession of all normal capacities, and with reference to the body, there was the tendency to stress youth and beauty, and equate good looks with virtue.
7. The historic roots of implicit immorality, as in the Old Testament, in which physical punishment and sin were closely interwoven.
8. Contrariwise, in later writings, physical destruction was regarded as mortification or purification.

9. Society's dictum of incompetence which resulted in loss of status for the blind who passively accepted this judgment, and confusion of status for the blind who were oriented toward achievement and a more active living pattern.

Obviously, the preceding discrete blindness limitating effects are essentially extrinsic and quite similar to those stated more generally by Professor Himes.

Seeming to combine the intrinsic effects in Category A and the extrinsic effects in Category B, Gowman included a third category.

C. *Decreased control over the self and the environment*:
1. The world was arranged for the sighted.
2. Environmental control and self-control were intimately related.
3. Blindness was a gulf which inevitably influenced the interplay of the self and physical and social objects.
4. Blindness subtracted dimensions from the world while adding cumbersome expedients which served somewhat to facilitate relationships (cane, dog, companion, reader, groping movements and touch).
5. No matter how vigorous and competent, every blind individual was forced into some measure of dependence where the mediation of a sighted person was necessary, especially in situations of concrete physical mobility.
6. There was a lack of social environment mastery since a blind individual could never be sure what anyone else was doing with looks, glances, gestures and grimaces. Blind persons could be, often were, isolated in a room full of people. Almost everywhere, a blind person could be easily avoided and usually had to wait for the other person to engage him.

The evident repetitiousness of the identified blindness effects does not detract from their common sense experiential validity. But the investigator continues to further emphasize his basic thesis of losses in social communication:

1. Direct physical contacts were generally taboo.
2. The losses due to lack of eye contacts.
3. The voice alone was relatively narrow and limited in comparison to voice-eye meanings.

In conclusion, Gowman identified those losses which affect the individual's entire security system because of decreased perceptions, decreased controls, and decreased communications:

1. General state of tension.
2. Social uneasiness.
3. Strain and anxiety in social situations.
4. Expenditure of extra energy on routine of living.
5. Decline in self-regard.
6. Shaking of the coherence of personality organization.[14]

Dr. Gowman seems to have set the pattern and format for the presentation of limitations and restrictions resulting from visual deprivation. In 1961, a prominent and respected worker in the field, Rev. Thomas J. Carroll, authored a book in which blindness was viewed as a multiple handicap. Like Dr. Cholden, Father Carroll stated, "Blindness is a death of a way of life that had become part of the individual. It is the end of acquired methods of doing things, the loss of built-up relationships with people, of ingrained relationships with an environment."[15]

Apparently, borrowing liberally from Dr. Gowman, Father Carroll classified twenty specific intrinsic and extrinsic losses, while presenting a sort of balance between the two categories and emphasizing their interrelationships. Quite like Gowman, the Reverend adds three extra considerations:

1. Change of roles, particularly those concerned with loss of decision in social situations.
2. Change of control of environment as related to loss of sleep at proper time.
3. Change in physical tone because of restricted mobility and continuous emotional strain.

Here, the author seemed to be leaning toward the extrinsic. His stated reference was to psychocultural effects of blindness.

Sufficient data has now been included to give the reader a comprehensive knowledge of the effects of blindness, as well as an appreciation of some of the deeper insights necessary for knowing

[14] *Ibid., pp.* 97-130.

[15] Rev. Thomas J. Carroll: *Blindness*. Boston, Little, Brown and Co., 1961, p. 11.

and understanding particular blind individuals. Another listing is being included, however, because the terms used refer to more commonplace observable behavior. Developed by psychologist Lee Meyerson, these resultants of visual impairment are:

1. Withdrawing, retiring, reticent behavior.
2. Lack of initiative.
3. Shy, timid, self-conscious, fearful behavior.
4. Obliterative behavior, refusal to recognize real conditions and limitations.
5. Hurt, resentful behavior.
6. Serious, thoughtful behavior.
7. Emotional and psychosexual immaturity.
8. Isolated, asocial behavior.
9. Unrealistic levels of aspiration, too high or too low goals.
10. Paranoid reactions, sensitivity, suspiciousness.
11. Craving for affection, love of praise, attention seeking.
12. Aggressive, competitive behavior, bravado.
13. Anxiety, tension, nervousness, general emotionality.
14. Artistic, phantasy behavior.
15. Behavior known as "blindisms."[16]

Obviously, some blind persons are relatively free from many of the enumerated blindness resultants, but for many, the effects are only too real. The specialized recreation center serves as a needed community resource for these many blind persons who cannot plod the ambiguous path between the sighted and the blind. Ishbel Ross said that it took the most vigorous and strongest to breast the stream.[17] Recreation in the specialized center can meet the recreation needs of these members of our communities who become inactive and isolated.

In 1956, the Bureau of Labor Statistics published the results of a nationwide survey of services to blind persons which showed that of eight major service classifications, recreation was the third most frequently rendered service. More recently, a prominent authority in work for the blind observed that "one of the roles of the agency

[16]Lee Meyerson: Somatopsychological aspects of blindness, *Psychological Diagnosis and Counseling of the Adult Blind*, ed. Wilma Donahue, New York, American Foundation for the Blind, 1947, p. 15.

[17]Ross, *op. cit.*, p. 6.

for the blind in the United States and, in fact, in most of the English-speaking countries has been developing and providing recreational programs for blind people in the community."[18] In 1959, testifying before a Congressional House Sub-Committee on Special Education, the Executive Director of the American Foundation for the Blind, Inc., stated that with regard to older blind persons, there was no program in the entire country that was realistically geared to meet their needs, and that perhaps the recreation center was one of the answers.[19]

Characteristics of Blind Persons Attending Major Specialized Recreation Centers in New York City in 1960

To plan specialized recreation center activities and experiences to constructively meet the needs of the blind adults who will be the participants, data concerning the individual's physical, mental, emotional and social characteristics should be known and utilized. It has been established that blindness is an individual matter, and that visual deprivation does not necessarily standardize behavior. However, the intrinsic and extrinsic effects of blindness interacting with other personal factors like age, general health, socio-economic status and education background, tend to produce certain identifiable characteristics which influence program operations.

Vision

Observational and impressionistic data place the number of specialized recreation center participants with usable partial vision at from about one half to three fifths of the membership. This is a significant finding because vision enables the individual to participate in a great many more activities, to be more mobile, to be more useful in a helping role, and possibly to exert a normalizing and integrative influence in the specialized blindness milieu of the center. It is essential, however, that members without usable vision be given whatever assistance is necessary in order not to exclude

[18]Irving Miller and Sherman Barr: *Recreation for Deaf-Blind Persons.* New York, The Industrial Home for the Blind, 1959, p. 1.

[19]American Foundation for the Blind: *AFB Bulletin,* No. 13, Legislation Series, April, 1959, p. 5.

them from any recreation activities and experiences which may constructively meet their needs.

Mention has been made of the tendency for the partially sighted legally blind persons to dominate program activities. The resentment and bitterness engendered in the totally blind members is quite real and too often justified. While professional workers may be intellectually certain of their goals, their own emotional reactions to total blindness unconsciously impels relationship with those members who can see. Sometimes members without vision are thus denied the full resources of the center. More importantly, this quite obvious occurrence is confirmation of the primary extrinsic reaction to blindness which the member experiences frequently enough outside the center, and which may be part and parcel of his attitude toward himself. At the same time, it is a mistake to obviously contrive attention and adapatation. The negative effect on the totally blind person is the same, although his reactive behavior may be different.

Age

It is estimated that more than one half of the blind are over sixty-five years of age. Blindness is more and more associated with longevity. The indications are that the specialized recreation center population will continue to become increasingly aged. Older current members happily continue their attendance. New older folks happily become members. The younger adults, amenable to vocational rehabilitation, tend to give up their center membership soon after they are placed in employment.

Extrinsic and intrinsic effects of blindness therefore have to be considered in the context of the aged membership, e.g., "Old age travels slowly, cautiously, and often fearfully. Age slows down most of life's processes: eyesight and hearing are not so acute, moving about takes more effort, details are often difficult to grasp and remember."[20] This general description is quite appropriate as it relates to many of the blind members. Of course, there are exceptions. Not all blind persons are so severely limited and not all older center members are so lacking in self-reliance.

[20]Morton Thompson: *Starting a Recreation Program in Institutions for the Ill or Handicapped Aged.* New York, National Recreation Association, 1960, p. 11.

Every person lives within the framework of his own resources. Basic needs are constructively satisfied when behavior is effective within the reality limits of a person's handicaps, rather than in a continuing and exhausting attempt to achieve the impossible. Hence, while blindness compounded by age may tend to make the atmosphere somewhat gray, the general tone should be, and can be, hopeful and optimistic. Learning about oneself and others, acquiring new knowledge and skills are interesting and stimulating experiences for almost all individuals.

Health

While blindness is, by itself, a physical handicap, it seldom occurs as an isolated physical phenomenon in young or old persons. Blindness is usually a symptom or effect of other bodily systemic difficulties like glaucoma, diabetes, and cataracts. Intake procedures must therefore include explicit medical information regarding the nature and degree of activity permitted and diet restrictions in relation to food and refreshments. It must also include instructions for first aid in emergencies, e.g., fainting, weakness, or injury; and the name and phone number of the doctor and nearest relative. A good health practice and a desirable center procedure is the requirement of an annual medical check-up.

Blind individuals who have little or no self-reliance, and who are confined and dependent, represent the very people for whom the specialized recreation center functions. However, an individual should not be included or continued in the center if he has other handicaps, physical and/or mental, which will seriously interfere with program activities for the other members. In this sense, the specialized recreation center is not conceived as a treatment center for blind adults whose degree of exceptional behavior requires medically directed psychotherapy in a clinical or treatment setting. The advent of social group work has made possible the inclusion or continuance of mildly disturbed individuals who can be given some special program attention. The specialized recreation center member who is physically blind only, is singularly rare.

Male and Female Members

The enrollment ratio of men and women in specialized centers is not significantly different from the proportions found in the sighted population generally. In the below thirty-five-year-old group, men slightly outnumber women; and in the above sixty-year-old group, women outnumber men. Sex is a recreation activity determinant. More younger men participate in sports and games like bowling, table games, skating, swimming and trips. Older men prefer arts and crafts, ceramics, singing, discussions and social dancing. Younger women tend to choose bowling, social dancing and dramatics; while older ladies select arts and crafts, ceramics, sewing, millinery, and clubs.

Most centers conduct co-educational programs, but opportunities should be present for activities in which only men or only women participate. For example, only women are found in beauty culture groups and in certain women's clubs. Activities like sewing, dressmaking, millinery, knitting, cooking usually attract women. However, older men participate in sewing, millinery, knitting and cooking. Most recreation activities can be conducted on a co-educational basis. However, there should be opportunities for single-sex activities when they are desired and when they contribute toward the objectives of the program. In one center studied, there were several all-ladies bowling teams, folk dance groups, and drama groups.

Economic Level of Members

Studies have confirmed the depressed economic status of blind persons generally. Approximately 90 per cent of the several thousand enrollees in six major specialized recreation centers for adults in New York City were reported to have marginal incomes of less than three thousand dollars per year. An estimated one-third were receiving public assistance. Only about 5 per cent were fully self-supporting. These data have significance in several ways. They indicate that most specialized recreation center members lack the resources to purchase commercial recreation services and/or equipment. Such factors are significant in relation to center fees and charges for membership, supplies and equipment, transportation and/or other services.

There has been a growing tendency to institute policies and procedures which will inquire more specifically into a member's ability as well as his attitude regarding payment for recreation services and supplies. These efforts are compounded by a philosophy which wants to expunge as many factors as possible from the stereotyped notion of the blind as inferior and/or pauperized, and concomitantly, to utilize the ego-strengthening effects which result when members are given an opportunity to decide whether they are able to pay. A realistic consideration pertains to the fact that about 90 per cent of the members are not in any position to pay for services or supplies. It is not unlikely that the cost of administering this aspect of a center program may exceed the income. It would appear, therefore, that such a decision should not be based upon the expectation of significantly reducing the budget.

Education

Current center memberships are made up largely of individuals who have not graduated from high school. This is not a startling finding, since census data indicate that half of those adults now over sixty-five years old have not completed the eighth grade. The implication for program planning is that methods of teaching, content, and quality of relationships need to be geared to the junior high school or early senior high school, with due consideration for education and understanding acquired through living. Perhaps a common error is the assumption that because the member is an adult, he is prepared for activity at the college level or above. Increased anxiety and failure are certain if program does not begin at the level of the member.

Religion, Race and National Origin

Some individuals react to their feeling of guilt for being different, unloved, unwanted, and despised by enlarging their own existing prejudices against blind persons of different religion, race or national origin. Their own inner conflict is intensified and revealed as over-aggressive criticism and unfriendliness. It has been glibly said that blindness no more unites blind persons than sight binds sighted persons together. On the other hand, a consciousness of kind frequently combines with aggression and reveals itself as reconciliation and appeasement. The many parochial facets of work for the blind persuasively suggest a common bond between and among blind persons. Certainly the intrinsic effects are largely shared by most blind persons, as well as the extrinsic.

In our society, blindness generally connotes a subculture group, and blind persons tend to have many similar needs which have developed out of their shared fate. Ascribed stereotyped status modifies individual needs and the result too often is behavior which verifies and strengthens the stereotype.

Positive use can be made of these common problems, fears, anxieties, frustrations, angers, and hopelessness. Professionally led forums, discussion groups, inter-faith and inter-racial cooperative projects, mass activities with nationality themes and customs, all can help to soften the encrusted prejudices of the members. Most significant, perhaps, is the atmosphere of administrative sincerity and genuineness on the part of all staff regarding respect for individuality and personal worth. Acceptance, friendliness, ease and honest interest lessen anxiety, fear and tension. Sometimes an upset member who continues to disturb the program may have to be dealt with administratively, perhaps referred for special help, or finally, expelled from the program.

Ability to Read Braille

Reading braille is a prelude to participation in many activities, e.g., cards, scrabble, anagrams, dramatics, bingo and others. In some centers, learning to read braille comes within the scope of program activities. The ability to communicate in writing has been found to be an important skill of the indigenous group leader.

Mobility, Outdoor and Indoor

Physical movement is essential for physical and psychological health. Activity has been identified as a fundamental characteristic of life. It has been wisely stated that a person is not in the world until he moves in it. Outdoor mobility, more commonly known as independent travel, is the predominant intrinsic restriction caused by blindness. Fear of injury and pain, fear of groping and identification as a blind person, fear of dependence, combine to immobilize and isolate the blind individual. Usually, there is a direct relationship between a blind person's need for recreation and his inability to get about. This rather obvious rationalization justifies the large expenditures for paid transportation. Extensive experience has shown that the organized recreation program is almost completely dependent upon the reliability of transportation for the blind persons who cannot travel alone.

Indoor mobility also affects program activities. Members who move fearfully, awkwardly, gropingly, cannot participate easily or safely in activities like bowling, swimming, dancing, or dramatics. Many such members continue to require assistance in going from one activity to another, or to the bathroom, despite planful efforts to teach them mobility skills and to instill confidence in their use. These folks just cannot risk themselves in physical movement.

Summary of Behavior Manifestations

Characteristic behavior manifestations identify those blind individuals who required the services of the specialized recreation center:

1. Inability to learn to travel outdoors independently.
2. Need for continued assistance in indoor mobility and personal care skills despite orientation and training efforts.
3. Possession of physical and personal traits which are disturbing to sighted participants in nonspecialized settings, e.g., disfigurement, poor posture, groping, grimacing, helplessness, withdrawal or aggression.
4. Desire to associate with blind persons because the individual derives comfort and security through sharing his feelings with others similarly handicapped, i.e., the risking of self and the meeting of latent dependency needs in an environment in which there is objective expectation and understanding of such roles.
5. Need for intensive motivation and assistance for the individual to participate constructively in recreation activities and experiences.

Again, there are individuals who neither need nor want the services of the specialized agency. A general appraisal of persons who are blind will be found useful in suggesting the need for specialized consideration.

1. Individuals who are making a socially acceptable, independ-

ent adjustment to blindness—those who have the internal and external resources to accomplish their daily tasks and gratify their essential needs.

2. Individuals who do not have the internal and/or external resources, or who are hampered in their ability to make the best use of their resources because of personal pressures and anxieties. These people ar unable to make decisions necessary to satisfactory functioning and tend to operate on a crisis basis in which they continually require external support.
3. Individuals with strongly impaired egos who can meet only their basic physiological needs, and who tend to be isolated and withdrawn. For these individuals, the trauma of blindness crystallizes neurotic potentialities, as would any crisis, and for them, blindness tends to be almost totally disabling.

To prevent individual debilitation, and to encourage habilitation and rehabilitation of those blind persons in need of enabling and supporting assistance, consideration should be given to the principles which follow:

1. There should be recognition that for some blind adults the specialized recreation center program may be needed only temporarily, while for others, the program may represent an optimal level of rehabilitation and often habilitation.
2. The specialized recreation center should not be composed entirely of visually handicapped persons. Such complete segregation would tend to overstress common individual and social hardships resulting from blindness and limit opportunities for positive and varying recreation experiences which link individuals with reality and society.
3. The specialized recreation center should planfully include selected, trained and supervised volunteer workers in order to maximize recreation experiences for the member. They should also provide educational and social experiences for the sighted individuals who, upon their return to the community, will act as emissaries of the center.

Chapter V

THE ACTIVITY PROGRAM

PRINCIPLES are implemented and objectives are achieved through the media of recreation program activities and experiences. Recreation, *per se*, encompasses limitless activities which meet the varied needs of individuals. Concern for the total personality of an individual and his constituent need for activities and experiences in many areas necessitates the offering of a wide selection of activities based upon the identified needs, interests, skills and capacities of the persons to be served.

Professional recreators have developed major categories of recreation activities for inclusion in balanced organized programs, *viz.*, (1) arts and crafts; (2) dance; (3) dramatics; (4) groups; (5) literary and language; (6) music; (7) nature and outings; (8) social events, and (9) sports and games. These categories are comprehensive but not exhaustive, and definitive but not mutually exclusive. They are obviously presented in alphabetical order, thus implying no inherent value priority in programs. The extensive scope of these categories offers quantitative as well as qualitative balance, i.e., action and passivity, large and small muscle coordination, gross and fine intellectual and/or emotional development, and opportunities for lower and higher levels of creative expression. Organized recreation center programs should include some activities from each of the categories, as these are desired by the members, and if the activities contribute in some measure toward center objectives.

Often, specialized center recreation programs are efficacious and therapeutic simply because a handicapped individual is provided regularly with an opportunity to be out of the house, and out of the way, on a constructive and anticipatory basis. An easing of household tensions is a notable concomitant of the blind person's involvement in out-of-the-home programs. Obvious improvement in attitudes, interests and skills further helps to better home situations.

Programs should include a variety of suitable activities, but they should also be people centered. Many participants in specialized programs require individualized assistance with their activity planning. It is precisely for this reason that specialized programs differ from regular programs in which members join by registration and then independently select their activites. Of course, some blind persons are able to select the activities in which they wish to participate, but most require some assistance.

For all participants there should be planful and frequent utilization of common human likes, e.g., the comfort of the familiar combined with the love of variety; the enjoyment of climaxing events like parties, carnivals, and shows with their constructive membership participation possibilities. Easy humor should permeate the programs because laughter has genuine strengthening values which few medicines can match.

Adaptations

Specialized recreation centers serving visually handicapped individuals require some adaptation of facilities, equipment, and materials. Yet, it is common experience that only few substantive teaching adjustments are necessitated by blindness, e.g., more detailed verbalized instruction, and the utilization of substitute sense stimuli, like handling ceramic, sculpture and craft pieces as suggestive models; or feeling a pinned hem or seam in sewing and millinery; or kinesthetically experiencing the instructor's movements in dance steps. It is important to have well-lighted activity areas with well-defined aisles and passageways between benches, tables and equipment to encourage independence in movement and to promote safety.

A great deal of staff time needs to be spent in planning and preparation. In activites such as crafts and dramatics, preparation time often exceeds member activity time. The wide range of membership interests, skills and capacities combined with the previously developed intrinsic and extrinsic effects of blindness necessitate a great deal of individualized instruction and assistance. Carefully selected, trained, and supervised direct service volunteers help to meet the need for intensive personalized help. Generally, as soon as a handcraft group exceeds four or five, at least one staff assistant is desirable so that members do not sit and wait for the help they need to get started. It is important also, to protect the activity leaders from exhausting and frustrating pressures which result when there are too many members in a group. Direct service volunteers are also very useful in the preparation of class materials as well as in giving needed individualized personal assistance to the members.

In addition to a wide variety of recreation activities from the delineated categories, programs should include novel activities which may be motivated by the presence of singular volunteers and/or handicapped members with special talents and capabilities. In one center, finger painting becomes a desirable recreation activity for a totally blind older lady who taught art and painting when she was sighted. For most blind adults, finger painting has not been a feasible recreation activity. In another center, bag punching intrigues and delights a group of younger blind adults through the leadership of a former boxing champion. In still another center, fencing is favored by a few agile members. The activity was introduced by a former Olympic fencer. And in another program, SCUBA diving is regularly taught by qualified American Red Cross Safety Instructors.

A word of caution is necessary regarding the public representation of member achievement. In some centers, partially sighted members with special talents happily paint credible scenes and portraits. The participants require special lighting, magnification devices and staff assistance, as well as their own enormous concentration and effort. Some of their paintings are then publicly exhibited with justifiable pride, but carelessly represented as the achievements of blind individuals, i.e., persons without vision.

Such ill-advised imputations are harmful to everyone. Totally blind individuals are made to feel uncertain, while members with usable vision feel hypocritical and defensive. Even worse, blindness stereotypes are perpetuated, and the community as a whole is confused. Whether considered as a denial of the reality of blind-

over sixty years of age. Even in centers in which social group work is the principal modality of operation, handcraft activities are utilized to get members active. Then, through discussion, cooperative craft projects are formulated. Such group projects may include the construction of decorations for special events and parties; props and costumes for drama presentations; sewing sleeping gowns for foundlings; knitting socks and sweaters for refugees, or rolling bandages for the disaster unit of a local Red Cross Chapter or civilian defense unit. These latter involvements in helpfulness to other community institutions have a particular significance in relation to the stereotypical notion that blindness means dependency and inactivity, a notion widely held even by many blind individuals.

Arts and crafts articles serve as tangible evidences of satisfactory achievement for the participant, the staff, and the community. Sincere, deserved recognition, via simple ceremonies and non-competitive rewards, strengthens the members. It also contributes to staff morale, and provides concrete products for use in positive public education and constructive institutional publicity.

Certain handcraft activities have been found to be particularly suitable for organized recreation center programs for visually handicapped participants. In alphabetical order, these include the following:

1. Basketry
2. Ceramics
3. Leather
4. Metal
5. Millinery
6. Knitting
7. Raffia
8. Rugs
9. Sculpture
10. Sewing
11. Tiling
12. Weaving
13. Woodwork

These thirteen arts and crafts activities will be considered in related groupings. For example, ceramics and sculpture activities are usually performed in one room and handled by the same staff members. Similarly, millinery, rug-making, and sewing are often combined in an activity room. In fact, in some small programs, in which physical resources are limited but the leader has teaching skills with several craft materials, many craft activities may be carried on in one craft's room at the same time.

Basketry, Raffia, Weaving, Rugmaking

Despite the association of basket making with stereotypical notions of blindness, reed is a material which flexibly lends itself to a large variety of simple and complex projects which can be useful and beautiful. A few fundamental skills enable many blind persons to work independently on their own creations. Many aspects of tactility and finger mobility are learned and developed when working with reed, raffia, straw, plastic, paper, and other materials which can be woven. The materials and equipment used in basketry are relatively inexpensive. Large shelves for reed storage and large sinks for reed soaking are required. In the context of an arts and crafts program in which many materials are being used the negative implications of making baskets has been found to be minimal or entirely absent.

Raffia is closely related to basketry. The basic materials are pliant plant fibers, twisted paper, or plastics. These materials do not require wetting. Chair seats and backs are favorite projects. Shopping bags and pocketbooks are also included in some programs. However, these projects are more difficult to accomplish because the frames around which the material is arranged are generally nonrigid.

Weaving is an activity in which cotton, wool or synthetic threads are interwoven to form cloth. The horizontal thread, referred to as weft, woof, filler or binder, is interlaced at right angles under and over certain of the vertical threads known as warp. Simple and complicated patterns are developed by manipulating the set positions of the vertical warp threads so that the binder threads go over and under designated numbers of warp threads to form cloth patterns. Differently colored filler and warp threads add to pattern variations and allow for great creativity and originality. The loom is mechanically designed to vary the horizontal movement of the binder shuttle through the vertical warp. There are manual and automatic looms.

Preparation of the loom by totally blind persons, that is, setting the vertical warp threads, is a difficult but not impossible task, if highly specialized marked devices are available. In recreation programs, the warp is usually set by the instructor. The blind indi-

Figure 1. Learned fingers evenly weave moistened reed around vertical reed spokes which have been set alternately through the border of holes in the wooden base.

vidual then performs the largely repetitive but satisfying horizontal binding of the cloth. Table looms are in evidence in many current specialized craft rooms, but only rarely is there evidence of active use. Often the looms are laden with dust while bearing evidences of attempts at weaving, e.g., some have just the warp with the beginning of binding, and occasionally completed material is wound around the cloth beam at the bottom. Apparently, the time and skill required, even in simple hand loom weaving, is more than can be handled in many recreation settings.

The presence of so many unused hand looms suggests caution in introducing this craft activity in the specialized program. But when this age-old, almost universal activity seems feasible and desirable, the donation of basic equipment and materials from other centers should be attempted before purchases are made. Some specialized centers have reported donation offers of manual and even automatic looms from institutions, firms and individuals. The larger looms take up a great deal of space and are notorious dust collectors.

A most elementary aspect of weaving is the setting of prepared loops vertically on a hooked frame (warp) and then handweaving similar loops horizontally (binder) to produce the familiar pot holder. This simple yet satisfying weaving project can achieve terrifying momentum with members turning out pot holders by the dozen. More complicated hand loom frames are available but one soon gets back to the aforementioned conventional pot holder loom.

Rugmaking is another weaving-related activity, popular with both men and women. Several types of rugmaking may be included in specialized center programs for blind persons. Inexpensive materials are readily available, little equipment is required, and once a member has mastered the relatively simple basic skills, only occasional supervision is required. Usually, rugmakers are able to carry on active conversations while busily making a rug. Final products often show expressive creativity in beauty of pattern and design, as well as utility. Rugs are braided, crocheted, or hooked.

Any soft fabric, jersey-like material, may be used in preparing the basic strips for braiding. Worn out tee-shirts and old pajamas are good for this purpose. One-inch strips of cotton or wool may also be used. Strips are then braided in traditional three-strand fashion, each strip under the second and over the third strand. Braided ends are attached to each other by looping or sewing. The braided materials are then sewn together with waxed button thread in the shape (round, oval, square, rectangular) and size desired. Differently colored strips are put in separate boxes so that the member can select particular color combinations and work them into distinctive designs.

In crocheted rugs, the material often comes from discarded nylon stockings. Strips an inch and a half in width are cut from the top to the bottom of the stocking. The strips are attached to each other by simple square knots. Other materials like cotton or wool may also be used. Aside from measuring tapes, markers and scissors, the only other equipment needed is a number ten or larger crochet hook. The rug is started with the basic crochet chain. The only change because of visual handicap is the necessity to remove the yarn from hook by hand, instead of just pulling the crochet needle from one loop through another.

Hooked rugs are probably the simplest to make. The inexpensive materials include three-inch strips of rug yarn, burlap or mesh backing, with burlap preferred, and a latchet hook. Once the simple technique of hooking is acquired, this activity begins to take on the momentum of pot holder production. Nevertheless, many older blind men and women derive apparent satisfactions through hooking rugs. Obviously, some of their recreation needs are met through this manual accomplishment.

Ceramics

Basic ceramics (modeling coil and slab building) introduces three dimensional manipulative activity which has significant learning and emotional release content for the blind participant. The meaningful fashioning of clay or similar material, such as plaster of paris, enables an individual to express his feelings while meeting many of his needs, which have been heightened intrinsically and extrinsically by visual handicap. Sometimes, individuality is startlingly revealed by the forms created, and often, a member's interpretations may serve diagnostically, to suggest other needed specialized services.

In addition to clay, grog, plaster of paris, etc., materials and equipment should include water, bats, glazes, and an adequate kiln or kilns with appropriate pyrometric cones, plus the usual assortment of clay modeling tools, basins, sponges, spatulas, rolling pins, wedging boards and damp closets for storage. Smooth, flattop tables, approximately twenty-eight inches high, are desirable.

Figure 2. Figures, forms, shapes, surfaces, sizes, materials provide the media for concentration, learning, emotional experience, and healthful creative expressiveness.

These relatively low tables allow the ceramist to sit comfortably while building up the creation, be it a simple ashtray, vase, or more complex project. Tables accommodating two or three workers allow for concentration, interaction and the necessary attention of an instructor.

The participants with usable vision may be able to complete their pieces up to the point of firing, including glazing. Many totally blind persons require assistance, with fine finishing and glazing. Members should be encouraged to do as much of the work as possible. The emphasis should be on self-help and genuine performance in relation to the individual's talent and capacity for learning and doing, while enjoying the process of learning and doing; then experiencing the pride of achievement through appropriate praise.

For the more sophisticated member who needs a different type of experience with clay, the potter's wheel offers a challenging and satisfying mode of expression and accomplishment. The feel of the wheeling clay in response to the treadle, the coordination of hand positions and finger pressures contribute to learning and enjoyment. Many basic sensory and emotional needs are met through this activity.

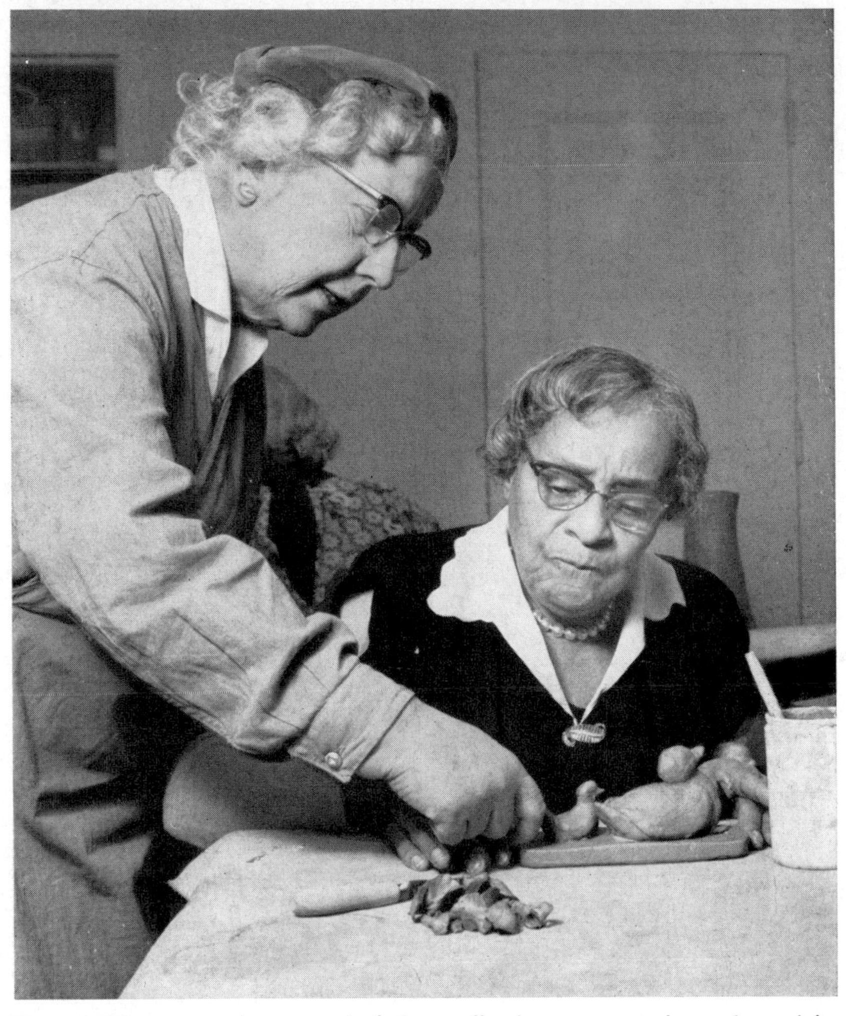

Figure 3. Memory, patience, touch, feel, coordination, concentration and creativity are clearly evident in this recreation activity.

Figure 4. The ladies are totally blind and the man is a partially blind instructor. Note the sensitive use of touch, the preparation of coils and their shaping into the little vase, and the well-shaped rectangular figure.

Kilnfiring often becomes a problem. Quickly getting the finished product back to the member is very important, particularly to the novice. Many ceramic rooms boast more than one kiln. Much glazing and firing are accomplished before and/or after classes. Completed ceramic pieces have to be fired at least twice, first to get the biscuit state and then after glazing. Firings take from twelve to fourteen hours and proper stacking of the pieces in the chamber is a task that requires knowledge, skill and time. Two or three weekly firings are maximum since the kiln takes almost as much time to cool. The average size of a kiln chamber should be fourteen inches by fourteen inches by twelve inches. In buying a kiln, it is best to get one with a large firing chamber and of course a source for 220 volts is required. An automatic timer is recommended so that the instructor can start the kiln after program. It must be reported that this practice of having the kiln on at night

Figure 5. Coordinated tactility combined with significant emotionality afford opportunity for the construction of sensitive and beautiful ceramic objects.

makes building and maintenance personnel nervous. They prefer the heating process during the day and cooling at night. The ratio of members to instructors should be about four to one. Ceramic pieces serve admirably as tangible demonstrations of accomplishment for the participants, instructors, administrators, board members and the community.

Figure 6. Variety of creations by blind members collected for proud end-of-season exhibit.

Sculpture

Sculpture is usually included in the ceramics activity for the few individuals with a talent and capacity for this mode of expression. Clay is used most of the time, although there is an occasional request for soapstone, wood and other materials. These sculptors become absorbed in their work in a manner that is truly consummatory and re-creative, particularly when a knowledgeable and skillful teacher is available to instruct and encourage the pupil. The intense concentration continues for weeks and months, as the fingers patiently explore the figures which are expressive of their ideas and feelings.

For the totally blind sculptor, a great deal of descriptive preparation and model handling is desirable and necessary. Of course, many factors affect the quality and quantity of initial instruction, e.g., interest, talent, intelligence, onset of blindness, tactility, and

Figure 7. The eighty-four-year-old totally blinded member enjoyed many pleasurable hours creating busts of himself, relatives and friends, leaving him little time for anxiety or boredom.

ability to concentrate and persevere. For the member with some usable vision, similar factors are significant. However, careful lighting and magnification devices now allow the patient member direct visual observation of the model, if one is used, or the continual examination of his own creation as it takes shape and form with expressive details.

Figure 8. A blinded lady is absorbed as she tries to express through clay, her visual remembrance of the past, her mother.

Leather

Leather is a widely used material. Leather projects are primarily in the form of commercial kits. While prepared projects undoubtedly limit variety and creativity, it is common experience that the range of available kits is sufficient to challenge the abilities and capacities of most members. When large pieces of leather are readily available through purchase or donation, necessary staff preparation of the material is extensive, and the material often becomes a non-commercial kit. Of course, members with usable vision can readily work on original projects, but they, too, require much technical advice and assistance. The instructor should evaluate the needs, interests, capabilities and skills of the members in the class. Then, in relation to available resources of supplies and of staff, a project appropriate for each member can be selected. The assignment of the same project to all should be avoided. Linking belts and lacing wallets should be utilized for the novice, and not continued repetitively, with the participants vigorously completing belts and wallets for gifts and for sales. Membership capacities and usable vision are important factors in determining class size. Usually, ten members require a leader and at least two assistants. Tables for four are recommended with a staff assistant, paid or volunteer, assigned to a table group.

Metal

Metal craft appeals to many members but, as a medium of expression and achievement, it is not as flexible as other materials. For most totally blind participants, projects are limited to hammered ashtrays, shallow vases, and candy dishes. The more capable members, particularly those with usable vision, can turn out metal pictures, earrings and bracelets. Some members can be taught to solder, even though they have no usable vision. Of course, great care is exercised in the use of the electric solder gun. Perhaps because the visually handicapped depend so much upon hearing as a substitute sense, the pounding and hammering in metal work disturbs other crafts workers and is hardly conducive to easy and fluid conversation. Metal crafts should be conducted in a soundproof room or in a room reasonably distant from quiet activities.

Figure 9. Variety of metal crafts shown at the end-of-season exhibit.

Figure 10. An end-of-season sewing exhibit demonstrates the individualistic interests, capacities, and skills of center members, as well as the varied and imaginative handling of varied materials.

Millinery and Sewing

Millinery and sewing are very popular with the ladies. In some programs, men have engaged in making simple items like aprons, smocks and pajamas. Several special devices enable many members to independently complete a greater proportion of the project, e.g., self-threading needles, measuring tapes stapled at half-inch markings, pinned borders, and of course, optimum lighting and appropriate magnification applicances for those members with some usable vision. Again, the emphasis should be on processes and interrelationships, rather than on products. Assistance should be offered when it seems genuinely necessary. The help offered should not be response to the self-pity, attention, and dependency needs of the member, nor should member assistance be the leader's response to his need to dominate and manipulate others.

Few members have the skill and vision to begin sewing projects from the raw material. As in most craft activities, a great deal of preparation is necessary, beginning with the cutting out of the patterns and ending with fine finishing, ornamentations, button-holes and zippers. The members who constructively need to do most of their own work should be given the understanding, patience and assistance they require, although at times, the reality frustrations of accomplishment without appropriate vision and capacity result in negative reactions for the participants and the staff. Generally, preparation time is about equal to activity time. A class of ten, which seems to be a maximum size, requires a leader in charge with at least two assistants.

A considerable variety and quantity of materials is required, bolts of materials, mill-ends, scraps, threads, needles, pins, staplers, scissors and measuring tapes. Adequate and orderly storage is difficult, particularly in a large program where many staff members need to have access to the materials and equipment. Millinery and sewing supplies are costly. Donations from manufacturers can supply much of the required materials but planful and continuous supervisory solicitation efforts are required. These efforts include carefully selected requests which inform the prospective donors about the organization, the program and its essential purposes, as well as prompt "thank you" letters for those who respond. Agency news bulletins and materials which inform rather than solicit help preserve a positive contact for other requests at appropriate times. Board members and special volunteers often serve as special personal contacts for the procurement of donated goods and equipment.

Sensitive awareness of recreation and center purpose is demonstrated when the donation of an expensive portable electric sewing machine is reluctantly refused because of the risk that some leaders may be tempted to take over and more quickly finish a hat, skirt or blouse for a member. The stereotypical specters engendered by blindness haunt so many and, in so many subtle ways, one wonders if the ambiguities in attitudes can be resolved. Constant supervisory vigilance and discussion are necessary to prevent excessive dominance of materialistic and neurotic influences in recreation activities. Professional recreation should be concerned essentially with processes through which human needs are constructively satisfied.

The products of recreation activity may have extrinsic worth as well, but when the financial motivations become too important, the members are engaged in work—not recreation. Certainly, there is nothing dishonorable in work; in fact, work is a highly prized American virtue. What is negative is the self-deception by the member, abetted by a sighted accomplice in the guise of a leader. The recreation leader cannot easily abide the notion that he has become a work foreman or that he may be indulging his fear and pity of blindness, so he compounds the deception by rationalizing his actions in the name of good intentions and dedication.

Woodwork

Woodwork classes are usually small, limited to three or four members who are usually younger males, that is, below sixty years of age. Wood is another flexible material which permits certain types of expressiveness and skills to meet recreation needs. The emphasis should be on fundamental hand tools like hammers, saws, screwdrivers, and hand drills. Power saws, drills and sanders may be used following careful orientation to their use and provided that all safety requirements have been learned. Power tools can often be fitted with special devices which enable a visually handicapped person to cut, drill or sand properly and safely. Recommended standard guides and safeguards are obtainable through a special service of the American Foundation for the Blind in New York City. Frequently, resourceful leaders devise methods and dies which help the blind participant to experience the use of power tools in constructing his projects.

In woodwork, members learn how to identify certain types of wood through senses other than sight, and their desirable use for particular purposes. Finger, hand, and arm coordination combine with touch to provide useful skills and knowledge which help in general orientation to reality. Most participants can learn how to use a braille ruler and how to mark or score a board in careful preparation for making a required square cut. Without sight, driving a nail straight is quite an achievement, expecially without marring the wood. The blind woodworker frequently checks the position of the nail and his strokes are more careful, lighter, and more numerous. Some members learn to use planes, chisels and miterboxes.

Always there is frequent touch reference and projects are completed more slowly.

A great deal of time is spent in sandpapering and preparing surfaces for stain, shellace and wax. Members seem to derive much satisfaction from constructing and feeling the shapes and surfaces of the projects. There are numerous positive by-products, such as increased knowledge of materials, tools, and equipment. The release of tension through expressions and concentrations outside oneself are worthy of note, as well as the tangible and intangible ego strengthening which results from effort and accomplishment which merit sincere praise.

Favorite projects include boxes of various sorts, utility, jewel, shoe-shine, and toy boxes. Stools and lamps are also made in many woodwork programs. Because woodwork classes are usually small, a skilled leader and one assistant are sufficient for effective instruction and supervision. Of course, adequate woodworking benches fitted with vises, one for each member, are minimum equipment requirements.

Tiling

Tiling (Mosaics) is an ancient art enjoying a renaissance in specialized arts and crafts programs. Only minor adaptation and assistance are necessary for most totally blind members. As usual, many partially sighted members are able to work independently after learning the fundamental principles and skills.

Basic materials include an assortment of wood, metal or glass containers, table tops, or any surfaces which can be decoratively covered with tiles. Tiles, assorted in size, shape and color, are kept in separate containers which are identifiable through distinctive shape, size and position, as well as through braille notation or other raised markings. White glue, in a convenient small plastic dispenser container, is used for the adhesive, and a clear lacquer spray for the final finishing. Grout is used to fill in between tile spaces and narrow strips of pliable materials (plastic) are useful in creating special designs and pictures. Equipment consists of awls for prying off and positioning tiles, sponges for cleaning tiles and work surfaces, and tile cutters, when special tile shapes and sizes are needed to construct particular patterns and designs.

For the beginner, so-called random tiling provides the most satisfactory introduction to this craft activity. Tiles of varied sizes, shapes and compatible colors are placed in one container. The participant then places and glues them in an individually expressive style. Gluing skills are easily learned. Hand and finger coordination and dexterity are simple, so that many members can experiment with several different types of projects.

Tiles with gauze backing which come in sheets can be cut in designs and patterns and glued right on to the surface to be decorated. While such short cuts facilitate completion, on the whole, flexibility and creativity are stifled. The member has his piece more quickly, the tiles are more even, and less effort, thought and feeling have gone into the production. It would seem likely that here, process has been sacrificed for production—and the participant must feel this.

Specific areas in which some sighted assistance is necessary include the arranging of materials, selection of appropriate projects, tile cutting and shaping to fill in gaps, preparing grout, cleaning off excess grout and the final light spraying of lacquer. Such assistance can come from trained, partially sighted members.

An interesting variation in tiling is provided by mixing in colored seeds, beads, and gravel with the tiles. These materials are set in thinly spread glue after the fill-in grouting process. Interesting effects have been obtained by shaking on gravel and then shaking off the excess. Ground glass, semi-precious stones, bits of shiny metals, such as stainless steel, or plastics may form novel and expressive patterns. Mosaics represent a flexible medium for creative experiences.

Summary

Arts and crafts activities dominate many specialized recreation center programs for visually handicapped adults, particularly for the members over sixty years of age. Undoubtedly, handcrafts have great meaning for the participants. Many recreation needs are met and skills are learned and/or rekindled. In addition, a considerable quantity of creative and expressive projects is produced, objects which have utilitarian and decorative values. Few will take issue with the mental hygiene therapy concept relating to consummatory experiences, nor with the dictum that individuals require manual accomplishment for normality and balance. Yet if recreation programs are really to be people-centered, should there not be some concern about the relative lack of incentive for physical mobility and membership interrelationships? Stated positively, more planful promotion and motivation should spark recreation activities which counter those prominent effects of blindness, physical immobility, and social isolation. Nevertheless, arts and crafts activities should occupy a balanced share of a comprehensive program while ingenuity and imagination are exercised to encourage physical mobility and socialization within the handcraft classes.

Visual impairment does not require fundamental adaptations in facilities or equipment. However, the nature and variety of member backgrounds, interests, skills and capacities combined with the intrinsic and extrinsic effects of blindness necessitate highly individualized assistance in learning and doing. The kind and degree of a participant's involvement in an activity is a function not only of the handicapped member's personality and capacities, but also of the staff member's understanding of recreation principles and objectives. It is in this connection that the term people-centered becomes much more than a cliché. Technical skills and teaching abilities are necessary. Even more important, however, is the conscious and continuous awareness that the member, not the project, is the prime concern of the endeavor. Exhibitable products can and should serve many legitimate institutional and administrative purposes but never at the expense of the meaning of process for the blind individual.

Dance

Because dancing is inherently a gay activity which meets so many recreation needs like exhibitionism, affiliation, play, activity, heterosexual association, rhythm, and many others, it is included in most specialized center recreation programs. Physical mobility and sociality are both encouraged and developed through dance activities. Many blinded members have had some previous, usually happy, experiences with dancing. The activity therefore serves as a positive link with the past. Most dances require no strenuous physical efforts and no adaptation to facilities or equipment. The atmosphere of fun, friendliness, movement and conversation is a welcomed respite from the prevalent grimness and isolation which is the common lot of so many members. Dancing stimulates physical tone and improves coordination and orientation. Members become more aware of themselves in relation to others and often there is significant improvement in posture, manners, speech and self-care.

Social dances can also serve volunteer recruitment objectives. Most direct service volunteers are women. Dancing is one basic skill they can offer which can be quickly, tangibly and positively utilized. Initial contact with blind persons thus occurs in an atmosphere of activity and enjoyment which quickly dispels some of their apparent initial apprehensions about "the blind." Subsequently, some of these dance volunteers can be directed into other program activities where there is great need for their various skills which they are eager to use for the benefit of the members. Usually, well-planned and well-publicized social dances attract considerable numbers of volunteers many of whom make up a kind of corps of knowledgeable center emissaries back to the community. These volunteers serve as community links with the members and with the institution. Their integrative and public education function is of great value to the members, to the center, and to the public which supports the program.

Center dance programs include two distinguishable groups, *viz.*, (1) formal and structured dance classes, sometimes classified under the term, eurythmics, and (2) organized social dances. Although organized and usually informal, a social dance may be relatively formal for special occasions like a St. Valentine's Dance, but it is not a formal instruction class.

Eurythmics

Specialized center programs include instructional classes in social dancing, folk dancing and square dancing.

Structured lessons in social dancing are well attended. However, as in arts and crafts activities, there is considerable range in member ability and capacity. High interests and needs are evident. Experience suggests grading of members into at least two gross capability groups. Real beginners and those members who apparently will continue to be novices for a long time should be in one class. The more experienced dancers and the obviously apt learners should be placed in the advanced class. Finer gradations can be made dependent upon the availability of staff, facilities, program time and the number of interested members.

It is common experience that some members in a beginners' class, those with "two left feet," little sense of direction, and limited learning ability, will continue to come to the class regularly all season, and season after season. They may make a little progress, but seem to derive meaningful satisfactions from the warmth, congeniality and physical effort. Obviously, many of their recreation needs are being met. For them, acquisition of specific dance skills becomes a minor objective. However, careful consideration should be given to certain associative factors, e.g., the meaning to these individuals of apparent continuous failure, the effect upon the members who are learning, and the understanding and handling by the leader who is in charge.

The member-instructor relationship must be friendly and mature when it becomes necessary to discuss a change to another activity for a participant whose presence in the group is no longer constructive for him or for the others. Sometimes, an insecure leader feels that this is his failure and rationalizes that the change to another activity may be a severe blow to the member's conception of himself. Recreators can recount instances of members unable to do a simple fox-trot box step after five seasons; or inability to play two basic guitar chords in D-major after six seasons; or the need for continued help in self-threading a needle and sewing a straight seam after eight seasons. These members must enjoy their companions and their leaders, but certainly a comprehensive and people-centered program can do a more constructive job of individual program planning. Perhaps special groups need to be organized for those members who find it too difficult to acquire discrete recreation activity skills.

Folk dancing and square dancing contribute variety and quality to the center dance program. Here there is opportunity for involving members with different nationality backgrounds and native skills. There are many simple Polish, Israeli, Balkan, and Scandinavian round dances which are feasible for visually handicapped individuals.

In folk and square dancing, the personality, knowledge and teaching skills of the leader are most important. For most members, these dances involve the learning of new movements and skills. Patient, explicit, and enthusiastic instruction is a must. Even in the simplest of circle folk dances, there should be ample provision for individual assistance by volunteers, staff or other members, for those learners who just do not understand particular maneuvers of the feet or arms. Because many folk dances tend to be relatively strenuous, even when the tempo is slowed, there should be sensitive awareness of physical exhaustion, especially for older folks. Some elderly members are not as sensible as alleged to be. The Mexican Hat Dance and the Hora are very energetic, the Hokey-Pokey and Hop-Scotch Polka are relatively relaxed folk dances. Marching formations are popular with many older members.

Square dancing is generally difficult or unhappily contrived and rigid when there is little usable vision among the members of a set. Some authentic squares can be adapted so that necessary physical contact is maintained as much as possible. Once a totally blind dancer has to be moved back to the desired position in the square, the rhythm pattern is destroyed and confusion reigns. Square dances which have been adapted for blind participants include Red River Valley, Duck for the Oyster, Grapevine Twist, Virginia Reel—and there must be others. Leaders can develop their own dance sets by combining basic folk and square dance maneuvers which are feasible for blind persons, for example, circle right and left movements, and in and out of center movements. "Do-si-do" is very difficult for individuals without vision, and "grand right and left" usually breaks up a dance. Still everyone is moving and laughing.

The tempo of music and instruction needs to be slowed, and simple but detailed directions are required. Also helpful are frequent tactile and kinesthetic teaching supplements such as allowing a member to feel the posture and movement of the leader, or having the instructor physically move the member in the desired manner. Sometimes these adaptations occasion considerable fun and laughter, particularly when members are shy or ticklish. It is desirable to isolate the poorly oriented, clumsy and slow learners to give them concentrated individualized assistance, in order to bring them to a minimum level of competency. They can then participate credibly with the group and feel a real sense of accomplishment and belonging.

Social Dances

Social dancing is a prominent activity in many specialized programs for blind persons. Many agencies for the blind, small and large, offer a service labelled "Recreation." In some locales, well-meaning service clubs indulge in similar patronizing efforts. The programs consist primarily of occasional get-togethers for as many local blind residents as can be transported to a suitable location for eats, entertainment and social dancing. These well-intentioned bread and circus motif shindigs are proudly conducted. Probably, many isolated and lonesome blind persons have a wonderful time. The break in monotony and routine is welcomed and perhaps even mildly constructive, except for those individuals who have learned to use blindness to meet their latent dependency need, or for those who have been vanquished and pauperized to acceptance of the inferior and helpless status.

Professional recreators look askance at such mass gatherings in which the blind persons are so obviously dependents who have to be fed, entertained and danced with. Frequently heard at these affairs are such indulgent exclamations as, "Aren't they wonderful!" and "They're so happy!" Motivations for these projects are certainly mixed, as are the results. But why should a professional worker have to choose? Significantly, the criteria for subsequent evaluation of these parties for the blind primarily include net attendance figures, blind and sighted; direct cash expenditures, and the volume of publicity accruing to the sponsoring organizations.

Social dances can play a positive role in meeting member needs and program objectives, when interested member-participants plan and conduct the dances, which are conceived as facets of total program activities. At such dances, designated staff, paid and volunteer, as well as center members are assigned to tactfully related themselves to the timid, insecure and unsocial members. Ignored, such

Figure 11. Informal dancing following a discussion group.

blind individuals are filled with even more anxiety and made to feel even more insecure.

A social dance problem which requires frank discussion and decision arises from the fact that sometimes a lack of female partners results in blind men having to sit out too many dances. Some of the more aggressive members will try to find a dancing partner by moving about the room using their hands rather than their voices to locate a dance partner. Even in the congenial atmosphere of social dance, this groping or moping practice is perilous. Planful use of available partners makes for a more constructive solution.

A related problem concerns the fact that the sighted and partially sighted ladies have to reverse the traditional female role of waiting to be asked to dance. In the specialized center, the ladies do the seeking and asking. Some blind men and many ladies find this role reversal difficult. Frank, open discussions, laced with common sense and wit, engender the friendly understanding atmosphere in which everyone is better able to deal with realities.

Figure 12. Young adults enjoy the formality and dress-up of special dances.

Appropriate music is an important ingredient of all social dances. Center dances provide a ready opportunity for music provided by members, who may volunteer or be paid for their services. When possible, reasonable payment for adequate musicianship is recommended, for there is hardly a more tangible method of showing earned appreciation. In many dance programs, phonograph records and recorded tapes are also used to provide the balanced variety of dance rhythms which will enable the largest number of participants to dance. Recreation leaders quickly learn that planful pre-stacking of records or tapes is advisable because it is difficult, perhaps impossible, to satisfy all the dancers with their conception of the best sequence of dance tunes. Of course, the younger folks prefer the latest fad tunes, while the more mature like the old standards. Almost everyone enjoys listening to good Dixieland jazz.

Smoking at dances presents a curious problem. Many blind folks take great pride in their ability to light their own cigarettes; and many blind individuals can advance additional reasons for continuing heavy smoking. Not the least of these reasons might be the social link with a worker, especially a volunteer, and perhaps there is a sub-conscious masochistic wish to punish and destroy oneself. Social and health reasons aside, cigarette butts make for annoying housekeeping and maintenance problems. Even an individual ashtray for each smoker might not solve the problem. Apparently, when a person does not perceive the ashtray, the tendency is to just reach down and crush the cigarette remains under the sole of the shoe. Discussions, pleadings, admonitions, regulations and prohibitions help . . . for awhile. Perhaps this should be considered a necessary special adaptation, except that administrators and maintenance supervisors are reluctant to accept this rationalization of an annoying problem.

Dramatics

Basic Values

Human needs may be satisfied in countless ways, through many media and on limitless levels of individual expression and involvement. Drama has a high priority as a recreation category in which varied forms of achievement enable the participants to experience the enjoyment of genuine creative activity. Adults who can be motivated to participate in drama activities are indeed fortunate.

Drama activities are uniquely appropriate to constructively satisfy many discrete needs which are so often frustrated and heightened by visual handicaps; needs such as achievement, recognition, exhibition, affiliation, cognizance, aggression, dominance, acquisition and others. Participation in dramatics helps to offset and improve some of the more visible behavior characteristics which so disturb the sighted, e.g., awkward posture, unnatural gestures, facial grimaces, shuffling feet, and groping hands. Interpreting, and acting-out roles in meaningful dramatic relationships seems to serve generally as a catharsis. Lessening of tension and anxieties are often evident as participants express feelings of release and increased confidence.

However, a note of caution must be sounded regarding a temptation to go into ecstasies about therapeutic benefits which result from participation in drama. Playing psychotherapist is inversely proportionate to the lack of professional competence and responsibility. Recreators and social group workers should not design psychodrama or sociodrama groups for seriously maladjusted members, unless there is adequate consultation with and supervision by qualified specialists in these highly specialized group therapy procedures.

A degree of self-revelation is inherent in most interpersonal role experiences; this is one of the basic dynamics in group process. However, the depth of involvement must not be dangerously traumatic for the blind individual who already is under considerable stress. Dissolving or weakening the emotional defenses of such an individual may result in grave and tragic consequences for everyone. Fortunately, there is great assurance in the experience that a group will function in protective fashion unless there is designed stimulation toward specific deep awareness for specific therapeutic purposes. This would seem to be the basic safeguard for many nondirected groups organized for alcoholics, drug addicts, prisoners, the handicapped, and other groups in which a common aberration distorts social functioning.

There is little likelihood of psychological backlash when the principal emphasis is on the situational interpretation intended by the author or recreation leader and when there is appropriate emphasis on stage and acting techniques.

Recreation dramatics is quite sufficient as recreation activity in its own right, without playing with psychotherapy. Recreation participants are exposed to literature, learn roles together, and communicate in new and different social configurations. They literally get away from themselves for a time, and somehow supportively share their new selves in constructive relationships. Only actors can really experience the quality of excitement and exhilaration which results when an audience acknowledges its appreciation by vigorous applause. Curtain calls and bows are deeply rewarding not only for the actor, but in the context of the specialized program, for the audience as well.

Program Content

Specialized recreation center drama activities range from a single workshop unit, with perhaps three or four participants, to numbers of graded workshops and production groups in which many members and staff are involved. Drama activities in comprehensive programs are usually considered in two separate groupings, workshops and formal play productions.

Workshops, whether introductory, elementary or advanced, are classes, in which members are taught basic expression, speech, movement, posture and position techniques. At the same time, intrinsic blindness mannerisms are corrected to the extent possible. For example, the posture of many totally blind individuals tends to be overly rigid. In movement, the arms are held stiffly at the sides, or a little forward so the hands and arms may serve to warn and protect. Unless a blind member is well oriented physically, the feet tend to probe and shuffle and there may be some active feeling or "moping" with the hands. Loss of visual and gesticulatory communications have to be surmounted through substitute sense cues. Members are taught how to move toward designated positions; how to locate a chair, couch, table, or other object; and how to reach them unobstrusively and as naturally as would a sighted person.

The workshop leader utilizes plots, scenes, situations and stories to stimulate imagination and to encourage response and relationship between and among the participants. Such exercises are generally referred to as improvisations. Here is a simple example of a workshop technique for illustrating mood and timing. The leader assigns three characters—a mother, her daughter, and the mother's friend. The daughter comes home to tell the mother and her friend the good news—she has passed her college examinations with high grades. In the next scene, the same characters are included, but now the daughter brings home bad news of failure. The inevitable change in mood and timing is dramatically significant to the members. They are impressed with the acting techniques which communicate these meanings.

A similar exercise has the leader or the members propose three words, objects and/or names. They then conceive and act out a situation involving these words. Interesting comedy and tragedy are often poignantly portrayed. Following such exercises, there are lively suggestions from the members for other situations and word groupings. In one workshop for older members, improvisations were based on situations involving the birth of a first child, or on long-ago visits to well-known places, and the actual or imagined presence at historic events. Formal performances do not result directly from workshop exercises. However, the members have frequent and varying opportunities to express themselves dramatically, to improve their stage techniques, movement, posture, speech, orientation, and general self-confidence, while enjoying the satisfactions which derive from doing and experiencing.

Then there are formal play production groups. The term *formal* refers to set plays with lines to be memorized and characterizations to be mastered in preparation for presentation to an audience.

Participants in drama should consummate their efforts before some kind of audience. For elementary groups, audiences may include fellow workshop members, friends, relatives, regular center members and staff. Advanced production groups should expand their appeal to include representations from the public. Sometimes, well-produced plays serve officially or covertly to impress board members, to educate the public, and for fund-raising purposes. Occasionally, administrative concern with this latter function insidiously alters the basic ingredients of freedom and flexibility which should characterize recreation activities. While the blind participants may still be creatively involved in a satisfying activity, extrinsic demands soon relate more to the needs of institutional power and process becomes subservient to production. When such emphasis is clearly evident, the drama group should become an adjunctive function of administration rather than of recreation.

One of the largest specialized recreation centers considers dramatics a major core activity. The program includes many elementary workshops and several production groups which seasonally present one or two full length plays. The senior group, "The Lighthouse Players" of the New York Association for the Blind, has earned wide national and even some international prominence as a theatre company of blind actors. The group comprises about seven blind individuals. Experienced and knowledgeable actors, they are assisted by a corps of helpers, *viz.*, an overall production supervisor, a professional director, stage manager, scene designer, guest actors, volunteer costume and prop assistants, ushers, maintenance men. They also have a host of indirect supportive service helpers who are involved with printing, mailing and publicity, as well as special committees for ticket promotion and administrative staff relationships.

The Lighthouse Players present two plays each season; one in the fall just before Thanksgiving, and one in the spring just before Easter. A play requires about twelve weeks of intensive preparation. Active rehearsals on stage are necessary for five weeks preceding opening night. The Players begin with regular rehearsals two evenings per week, which last from two to three hours each. Extra rehearsals are held, as needed, the week before opening. Each play is given on four successive evenings, with a matinee on Sunday. Audiences average around three hundred persons for each performance. Tickets are nominally priced at two dollars. The gross cost of a play is about five thousand dollars. The net cost is approximately two thousand five hundred dollars. This does not include the account cost of services given by the administrative and clerical workers who process the bills and receipts, and the public relations personnel who utilize the activity for public education and publicity. Lighthouse plays have been reviewed by major Broadway drama critics and given press, radio and television coverage. Often, celebrities accompany board members to first night performances, and some board members arrange pre-performance dinner parties.

The extensive experience of the Lighthouse Players has resulted in a catalogue of suggestions which can serve as guides for production dramatics in specialized recreation centers for blind adults.

Member Selection

The selection of members for participation in production dramatics should be based on the criteria which follow: (1) needs of the member; (2) dependability and responsibility in relation to class and rehearsal attendance (independent mobility is a great asset); (3) adequate intelligence in order to be able to understand characterizations, plots, relationships and communication; (4) ability to read braille, memorize lines and be responsive to auditory cues, and (5) reasonable physical presentability on stage in relation to mannerisms such as groping and grimacing. These qualifications reflect administrative and public relations influences upon the activity. When activities are primarily recreational, the principal concerns are with the participants, i.e., their needs.

Play Selection

Appropriate plays are difficult to find because so many factors must be considered. Theory and practice suggest these pros and cons:

1. Play content should not deal with blindness or other physical handicap.
2. Comedy, melodrama and mystery are preferred to tragedy or heavy drama.
3. Well-written plays with swift sophisticated dialogue are better than simple, dull plays with slow lines.
4. Plays with moderate physical movements are easier than those with excessive and violent actions by the blind actors.
5. Plays with too much pantomine and other forms of nonverbal communication should be avoided.
6. The blocking of plays should have the blind actors generally move away from stage-front (a rubber mat, about thirty inches wide, running the length of the front of the stage is helpful as a safety device).
7. It is advisable to block the play action so that as often as possible, an actor with some vision is somewhere on stage in scenes in which totally blind actors are involved in gross movements.
8. Simple uncluttered sets with a minimum of exits and entrances are preferable; single scene or, at most, one scene change is recommended.
9. Heavy furniture, tables, chairs and end tables, secured to the floor with a few tacks or nails around the legs serve to prevent upset and confusion from occasional miscalculations in movements.
10. Inconspicuously tacked-on rugs and runners leading to exits, entrances, and important stage positions are helpful.

The early availability of parts in braille is crucial so that the blind actors may quickly learn their parts. They can then devote major attention to characterizations, gestures, facial expressions, movement, cues and communication with actors and audience.

Figure 12a. The four actresses are totally blind, as is the actor with his arm around the girl's waist, in this delightful English comedy of marital mix-up, "Here Today" by George Oppenheimer. Note the simplicity of the set, the runners to the exits, and the uncluttered stage front.

Drama Staff

Perhaps even more than in other recreation categories, drama activities require technically knowledgeable personnel. Even in elementary workshops where improvisation is the principal method, the leader must know something about theatre and acting techniques. Members are quick to detect, respect and respond to informed and experienced competence.

A successful coach or director respects the individuality and potentiality of each member. While he may be enthusiastic about the possible qualities of performance which can be developed, he never loses sight of the reality limitations imposed by the effects of blindness in relation to the art of acting. A poor drama leader, who has to meet his own insecurity needs, will inflate the egos of the members and perhaps give them a false and temporary feeling

Figure 12b. The classic play "Skin of Our Teeth" by Thornton Wilder, gave seven blind actors and actresses tremendous satisfaction through opportunities to communicate interesting ideas as well as to relate to each other and sighted guest actors.

of exultation and achievement. The denial of reality is seldom successful, and self-deceit is no positive service to the handicapped individual. Precisely because drama activities can be used so constructively to meet many human needs, careful staff selection is necessary.

Center programs which include several workshops and production groups should have a full-time worker on a leader-supervisory level. One need but study the credits given to the supporting specialists and technicians in professional plays, television shows and movies to realize the size and complexity of formal productions. A production supervisor needs to coordinate the efforts of the director, coaches, stage manager, scene designer, lighting assistant, line prompters, guest actors, props and costume helpers, and a host of other workers concerned with notices, signs, publicity, tickets, numbered seats, ushers and receipts if tickets are sold. After a show, there are congratulations, parties, and plans for more workshop learning. Finally, the supervisor accounts for expenditures and receipts, evaluates the entire operation and reports to administration. A competent drama supervisor is a necessity.

Group Activities

Man is as much a social creature as a physiological entity. Many basic human needs are created from and satisfied through group experiences. The group is the normal setting in which people meet similar individuals with whom they can share common concerns revealed in terms familiar and acceptable. A group that has some degree of cooperative activity toward a shared goal inherently engenders a protective and supportive atmosphere in which the members experience a consciousness of kind that enables each to clarify his own expectations a little more realistically as well as to assess his own anxieties a little more objectively. The realization that one is not alone with his problems and that there are others who seem to have had to handle even greater difficulties tends to allay one's own fears and anxieties.

Even the very timid soon dare to risk making tentative suggestions, and after awhile, they are able to reveal some of their frustrations and burdens. Suggesting and listening, helping and being helped are the dynamics which make groups an important aspect of organized recreation programs. At the same time, many other discrete recreation needs are also met. Their satisfaction makes the member eager to continue and enlarge his participation in group activities. The small group provides a particularly appropriate milieu for the isolated individual who has not previously experienced group interaction.

In the specialized recreation centers, two types of groups are generally observed. Before differentiating them, the concept of the group should be clarified, i.e., a group consists of two or more persons who interact with each other, and whose particular relationships have sufficient structure and content to distinguish them as a separate entity from other groups or activities. In this sense a plurality of individuals may or may not be a group. Groups develop out of staff and/or member planning. However, there is no validity to the assumption that a group inherently satisfies recreation needs constructively. In other words, a group *per se*, is not necessarily a good thing. In a recent end-of-season report, a Recreation Director concluded that the members of a senior citizens group just wanted to sit around and regale each other with tragic accounts of their operations, isolation, inactivity, suffering and the indifference of their children, relatives and friends. One could feel not only the deepening despair of the older folks, but also the helplessness of the recreation worker who tried to obtain some solace by rationalizing that the members wanted to do this. Organized recreation should not compound tragedy.

The dominant type of group in the specialized recreation centers is commonly identified as the special interest group—and there are scores of them, e.g., bowling clubs, fishing clubs; folk song groups, choral groups; welcoming committees and program committees; ham radio clubs, chess clubs, public speaking clubs and a host of others. These are undeniably groups, i.e., they have two or more members who are aware of each other, and who interact in relation to common interests and purposes. There is sufficient differential structure and content to distinguish one group from another, and from other activities. Special interest groups may vary in size from a few members to more than one hundred. They meet regularly, exhibit vigor and variety in their activities and accord the participants many opportunities for meeting their recreation needs.

The second type of group found in specialized recreation centers possesses essentially the same general ingredients, but is differentiated by one important factor, i.e., the inclusion in the group of a leader who is a professional social group worker. In his social worker role, he planfully and purposefully directs group action in order to achieve designed individual and group interactions. The dynamics of the particular group relationships are understood and utilized to meet constructively the needs of individual members and the needs of the group as an entity.

In the first type of group, the leader is usually a recreation worker. As a professional worker, he is trained to understand group dynamics and individual recreation needs. Nevertheless, his focus is directed principally toward problem-solving in relation to the special interests of the group, and toward the development and use of indigenous leaderships within the group. These are noteworthy and constructive recreation center goals. Frequently, however, professional staff is not available for assignment to all groups, and reliance upon relatively untrained and/or indigenous leaders becomes the pragmatic solution which is then rationalized as the best answer.

Indeed, a group is not necessarily a good thing. Poorly led groups can be deeply destructive to individuals, despite regular meetings and functions which present a picture of harmony and activity. In their contacts with the public, such groups may strengthen and perpetuate blindness stereotypes which the center is trying to weaken and eradicate. The aims and objectives of the specialized recreation center necessitate professional supervision of all groups with appropriate opportunities for self-governing clubs to function as independently as possible in a manner which will foster achievement of center objectives.

Such professional supervision need not be constant and continuous, nor interfere with the normally understood prerogatives of internal club procedures and practices. The nature and degree of supervision can be worked out jointly with the officers of the club, as long as they accept in good faith the purposes and objectives of the center.

Some specialized recreation centers are fully committed to small group work as the principal modality upon which the activity program is designed. In such centers, recreation activities serve as the interest elements which help to associate individuals one with another. However, the most effective achievements are alleged to be those which result from the interpersonal relationships which are planfully stimulated by the social group worker. Obviously, social work groups tend to be smaller in size than the clubs, and while the leader's role is flexible, he is ever present and observing. Not every group requires a social group worker, but the specialized recreation center member is likely to benefit from participation in groups led by social group workers.

Social group work is particularly useful in dealing with members who have difficulties in social relationships. Sometimes, however, social group workers become so preoccupied with social skills that they neglect the obvious interest of the members in concrete recreation and adult education activities. The group then tends to become a contrived exercise in verbosity, which is frustrating for all.

The limited availability of qualified social group workers and the limited finances to engage as many as needed make discussion of their indispensability artificial and academic. There is little doubt, however, that recreation centers for blind adults should include social group workers, because the most predominant extrinsic effect of blindness is social isolation. The milieu of a peer group, i.e., a group of blind individuals, is most conducive for directed discussions of realistic problems arising out of conflicts caused by maladjustments to ill-defined role requirements. It is quite common experience that blind persons delight in castigating the sighted for lack of understanding, frequently referred to as "stupidity." Professional leadership is essential if the activity is not to become a destructive "flaying of a dead horse," in which the principal products are debilitating frustration and bitterness.

To safeguard group functioning, the recreation leader should beware of excessive concentration on goal achievement, particularly if the cooperative activity is directed toward materialistic ends or recognition awards. The leader should be sensitively aware of the relationships among the members because the group has a potential for destructiveness too. There should be time for the leader to know each individual member and how he sees his status and role in the group. Finally, the leader should be aware of his place in the group so that he can plan the degree and quality of his involvement. These are high order requirements for even a professional worker, but they are essential for the most effective functioning of a method of working with individuals to achieve center objectives.

Literary and Language Activities

Many intrinsic and extrinsic restrictions resulting from blindness may be lessened through activities which facilitate contacts and links with reality. Too often, blindness results in withdrawal and isolation from people and from things. Linguistic symbols occur in every phase of human endeavor and communication with oneself and with others is vital to sanity and health. Language is both cause and effect in socialization. In the cauldron of group dynamics, language is the primary tool which relates and connects people and ideas.

Some of the activities found in this category may appear more appropriate for inclusion in the previous category, "Groups." Their presence in this category denotes tool or method of receiving and/or imparting knowledge as the primary criterion.

Fourteen specific literary and language activities have been found present in specialized recreation center programs:

1. Braille
2. Debates
3. Forums
4. Languages
5. Lectures
6. Library
7. Newspaper
8. Public Speaking
9. Reading
10. Spelling
11. Typing
12. Writing
13. Phone-dialing
14. Cane travel

Some of the preceding activities, such as braille, spelling and typing, may seem more scholastic and academic. Class waiting lists and earnest requests for more classes attest the avid interest of the members for participation in these activities. In the classes, content is highly individualized and teaching methods are flexible. There are no formal achievement goals, and each member is encouraged to acquire at least elementary communication skills. Accomplishments are praised but slow progress or failure is understood and carefully handled. There is no pressure. The atmosphere is easy. The members enjoy working and trying to acquire knowledge and skills.

Braille

Braille intrigues many members. Apparently, following sufficient acceptance of blindness, and an awareness of the relative simplicity of Louis Braille's six dot cell, many members want to acquire this useful reading skill. Of course, actually learning to read fluently is not so easy; and too often, older fingers and weary brains are not adequate for the task. However, even if only thirteen symbols are mastered, i.e., from one through ten, the letter "k" for

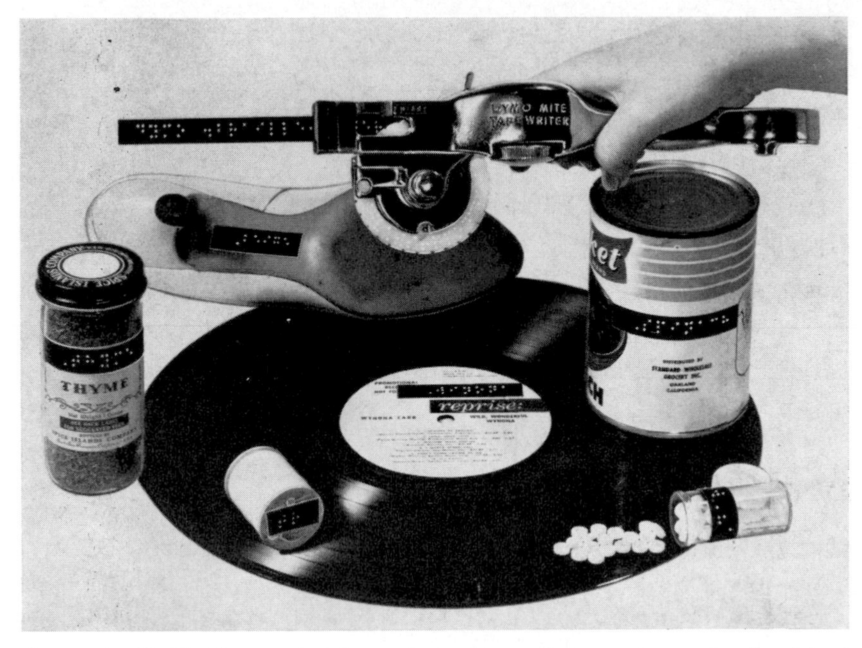

Figure 12c. Braille Dyno-Mite Tapewriter with regular print letters for the sighted and some labelled recreation center and home items.

king, the letter "q" for queen, and the letter "s" for spades, an extensive array of useful solitary and social card games becomes available to the member, inside and outside the center. Bingo is very popular with the members, just as it is with many sighted folks. Again, only the first ten braille symbols are needed for independent participation in this game, in the center and in the community.

Braille reading is necessary for memorizing scripts in dramatics. The ability to take notes in braille is often a significant factor in identifying members with initiative and leadership potential. Braille reading and writing open a wide avenue of contacts which help to keep a blind person in the stream of life. One can subscribe to numerous free braille publications. Receiving mail which you read yourself has unrealized ego-strengthening ingredients. Braille thus helps to prevent painful losses in status.

A Dyno-Braille-Tapewriter has been developed and is available from the American Foundation for the Blind at a cost of about $28.00. This device enables sighted persons, staff and friends, who do not write braille, to turn out brailled labels which can identify phone numbers, room locations, phonograph records, bingo boards and almost any object with a firm surface. Independence can thus be encouraged and the dividends in pride and self-respect are significantly evident. In some instances, brailled labels have motivated the learning of braille for card playing and reading.

Debates, Forums and Lectures

Debates, forums and lectures are differentiated by form and structure of activity rather than by content. The nature and purposes of a group determine the particular form and content of the information presented. For example, debates require knowledgeable leadership and relatively sophisticated members who delight in the more formal discussions of significant and controversial subjects. Forums tend to present informed speakers who allow sufficient time for questions and discussion; while in lectures, most of the time is allotted to the speakers. The range and depth of member questions often surprise guest speakers, even though they have been oriented and prepared. Somehow, their expectations continue to be influenced by the pervasive ghosts of tradition regarding "the blind."

Languages

The thrill of acquiring knowledge and skills, combined with necessity and the desire to be part of one's community, can be observed in specialized recreation centers where the members have asked for lessons in Spanish. Economic realities and general immobility keep many blind individuals resident in neighborhoods which are in transition. These members want to understand and relate themselves to their new neighbors; and another recreation activity comes into being.

Reading Groups

A special caution is advised with regard to "reading." Some volunteers, with the best of intentions, wish to contribute that ability which makes the least demand upon them, i.e., physical sight. In other areas this might be a blessing, but in the specialized recreation center reading group, the volunteer who "just reads" is deadly. The material should be appropriate for the group, but even more important is the ability of the volunteer to critically discuss content, style and author. Then the activity sparkles.

Typing

The desire, persistence and ability of many members, of all ages, to learn to type, principally for personal communication, is additional evidence of the member's need to continue or renew his status and links with his society, to be challenged, to acquire new skills or relearn old ones, and to go on doing. There is the hurdle of acquiring a usable typewriter for home practice. However, the benefits to the handicapped person and to the members of the family and friends are so evident as to make this problem readily solvable. Many local fraternal, religious-social and service community organizations will help to acquire usable typewriters for blind individuals. Corporations are often interested in providing their discarded but usable office equipment for such purposes.

The basic instruction methodology is the same as for sighted learners except the tempo is slower, and there is more visual inspection and correction of completed work. The only additional device found helpful is an embossed keyboard chart which can be purchased from the National Institute for the Blind, 224 Great Portland Street, London, W-1, England. Perhaps by the time this book is published, the American Foundation for the Blind will stock typewriter keyboard charts.

Script Writing

Script writing is desired by many literate blinded members. They want to continue using their communication skills and certainly every such link with normality should be encouraged and strengthened. There are numerous devices which serve as writing guides, *viz.*, folded cardboards which are placed beneath the regular writing paper, sometimes referred to as Venetian Blinds; rigid or flexibly lined frames which are placed on top of the writing paper, and boards with a guide line which moves at regulated intervals up and down (Marx Board). These devices are intended principally for adventitiously blinded individuals who wrote when they could see. The obvious function of the device is to help the individual keep his writing horizontal.

The more complex form of script-writing instruction, in specialized recreation centers, concerns those blind members who never saw or who were blinded early in life and somehow, never were taught regular written script. Some of these folks are facile in braille, but they cannot sign their names. As life becomes more complex and automated, there are more situations in which adults are required to identify themselves by signature, e.g., bank accounts, personal checks, voting, post office receipts, application blanks, membership cards and many others. Again we have an activity which directly involves member dignity, self-concept, links with the community and normalcy. Thus another activity is included in program, more adult education in nature, but necessary and proper in the specialized recreation center.

The goal of script writing for these members is usually personal signature, although a few go on to laboriously learn the entire alphabet. Various devices have been used in instruction. One of the best examined is a board similar to the type used in scouting on which different knots are demonstrated. Round plastic lacing, about one-sixteenth of an inch thick, has been shaped into form-related groups of letters, and attached to the script board. Those acquainted with the earlier Moon-Type embossed system will recognize the similar design.

One of the boards used at the New York Association for the Blind, was developed by a volunteer worker, Madam Fernand Pisart. The first line contains six letters: l, e, b, h, k, and f. In ordinary script, they all are begun with an upward loop. The second line has six letters which are essentially circles or part circles: a, o, d, q, g, and c. The third line includes seven letters which begin on the line, go up half-way and come back on, or almost on, themselves: i, u j, v, w, p, and y. The fourth line also includes seven letters: n, m, r, z, t, x, and s. A fifth line lists the numerals one through the zero of ten, and a sixth line portrays the basic punctuations: period, comma, semi-colon, equal mark, colon, quotation marks, parentheses, dash, exclamation point and question mark.

Teaching script writing to a totally blind individual who has not known regular lettering is a formidable challenge. However, the objectives are well worth the effort, unless continual failure dic-

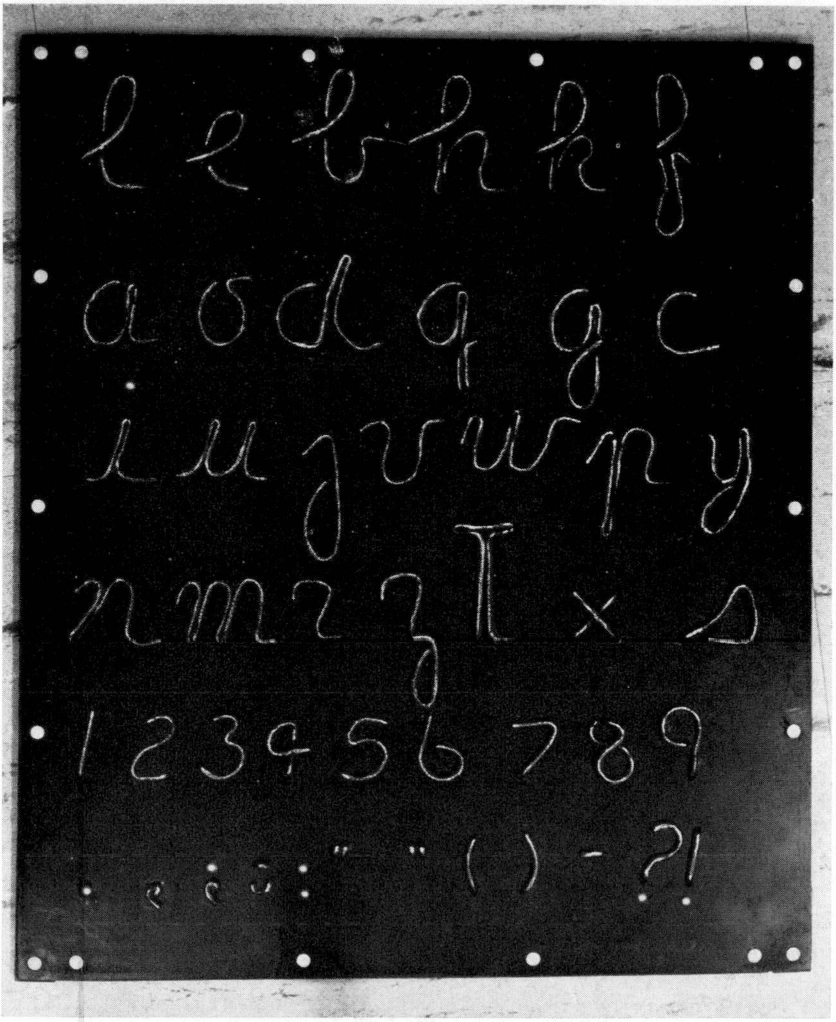

Figure 12d. Pisart Script Learning Board associates the basic form of most of the letters in the alphabet.

tates a halt. Then it is best to concern the individual with just personal signature as the ultimate goal.

There are many devices to enable a blind person to produce an acceptable signature which is in the proper place on a form, e.g., elliptical aluminum (round or flat) signature frames, metal slates with sections for name and address. A bank in New York City prepared a special thin aluminum stencil for their personal checks and the blind customer quickly learned the spaces for the date, payee, amount, and signature. What price independence! Recreation makes its contribution.

Many of the devices mentioned are obtainable from the American Foundation for the Blind. There is also a pamphlet on script writing which describes other approaches and methods.

Peripatology

Peripatology is the name given to the science of travel. Many specialized recreation center members are eager for information and skills which will help them move about a little more securely. They may just want to be able to get outside and walk around the block independently. A room or even an apartment beings to close in after awhile. Peripatology, while not an extensive technology, is the province of adjustment or vocation training in rehabilitation. It is best, therefore, to enlist the direct assistance of peripatologist. If this is not possible, a selected staff member can be taught the fundamentals of cane travel. Because one of the principal effects of blindness is restricted mobility, cane travel becomes an enormously desirable recreation activity. An individual is more in the world if he moves in it. This is a primary center goal. Structured lesson plans in cane travel can be obtained from many state rehabilitation agencies, from the Office of Vocational Rehabilitation in Washington, and from some local voluntary agencies like The Industrial Home for the Blind in Brooklyn, New York.

Music

Music has the power to take a person out of himself, out of the humdrum of day-to-day existence, and to arouse in his heart the most joyous and noblest emotions. Through music, he can recreate for himself, and make part of his experience, the excitement, the despair, the joy, or whatever emotion impelled the composer to write the music or the folk to improvise it. Through music a person can attain the quintessence of beauty, walk the Olympian heights of nobility and exultation, or drain the dregs of remorse and anguish. The essence of music is life itself.[1]

[1]Charles Leonhard: *Recreation Through Music*. The Ronald Press, 1952, pp. 5-6.

Anthropologists allege that music preceded language in the development of human expression and communication. Responsiveness to music seems to be a basic human characteristic.

Although there are no scientific data to support the fact that individuals without sight are gifted with special talents or abilities in music, organized, specialized recreation center programs include many music activities. Activities in this category require little movement, little exertion, and provide a variety of qualitative levels of involvement and of expressiveness. These characteristics promote their popularity with members.

Some recreation center programs even include formal instruction in piano, accordion, saxophone, clarinet, violin and other instruments. Such activities are usually not perceived as recreation activities, because of the necessary disciplined application and study. However, within the pervasive atmosphere of voluntariness and flexibility, these formal music lessons seem to properly belong in the recreation program; and the activity meets the expressed needs and desires of the members. Even for those musical instruments usually regarded as characteristically recreational, e.g., guitar, autoharp, recorder, and harmonica, some talent and disciplined applicability is required.

The setting, pace, and ready acceptance of whatever progress the members can make designate the activity as recreation. In this connection it is important that the leader and/or teachers be sensitive to the implications of failure and frustration when member progress is nil over a long period. The activity may then become more negative than positive. Recreation leaders are sometimes reluctant to suggest another activity in which the member may experience the satisfaction of achievement; and at the same time, the member hesitates to confirm his inability. The sessions continue long after recreation values are dissipated.

Music activities usually included in operating specialized recreation centers follow:

1. Autoharp
2. Bands
3. Chorus
4. Community Sings
5. Folk Songs
6. Guitar
7. Harmonica
8. Music Appreciation

9. Musicales
10. Recorder
11. Rhythm
12. Ukelele

Autoharp

The small five-chord autoharp is an excellent instrument for beginners. A simple chord is formed by pressing the corresponding chord button. The tone quality is good. A member can accompany singing after a few lessons. The five-chord autoharp costs less than twenty-five dollars. A larger instrument with twelve chords is also inexpensive. Home practice is simple. Information regarding purchase can be obtained from Oscar Schmidt International, Inc., 87 Ferry Street, Jersey City 7, New Jersey.

Bands

Abundance of leisure time encourages many blind individuals to undertake formal music lessons. For those who are learning to play band instruments, the opportunity to practice in a band group is eagerly sought. Positive interpersonal relationships and friendships are formed. The cooperative and rhythmic experiences are highly desirable and satisfying. A center band is a kind of culmination of conscientious effort and practice, just as *the play is the thing* with members in dramatics. The bands often include members who possess music skills acquired before blindness. Sometimes, skilled sighted volunteers helpfully contribute form and quality to the music. These bands may be used at center dances and entertainments. For a few members, band practice has vocational and remuneration connotations, but for most, band practice is an enjoyable recreation activity. Necessary minimum equipment includes a piano and a set of drums. Some care is necessary to locate the practice room away from activities which may be disturbed by the music. Once the band achieves some cooperative competence, continuous leadership is unnecessary.

Choruses

Choruses, glee clubs, and community sings should be regular recurrent program activities. Almost everyone can sing. Singing is individually expressive, as well as communicative. Singing tends to relate and unite people. Many levels of participation are possible, from the disciplined formal chorus for which one has to "try-out,"

Figure 13. A group of men sing out an old-timer with evident gusto and enjoyment.

to the informal "Mitch Miller" type of community sing. Only a few members have the skill and will for the structural chorus, but several specialized recreation centers have such high caliber groups. The members derive great satisfactions from the technical achievements, as well as from the recognition they receive within and outside the center. Such choruses serve as public education media for the centers and for blind persons generally. Of course, there is the danger of perpetuating the stereotype of the blind musician beggar or the blind musician genius. One is again apt to hear "Aren't they wonderful!" However, this reaction is inherent in every achievement by blind persons. Patronizers are useful and educable. Defensive attitudes can be directed away from the members while the resources are used to strengthen them.

Glee Clubs and Community Sings

The informal glee club and the larger community sing groups are the mainstay of the center singing program. The knowledge and enthusiasm of the leader are essential; and unless the leader is a rare one, planning is necessary. The content should include the favorites which almost everyone in the group knows. Despite an occasional grumble, the members like to learn new songs, or the complete lyrics of old numbers. Variety is important because of the range of individual favorites. Proper accompaniment should be provided on piano, guitar, accordion, banjo, ukelele, autoharp or harmonica. Some of the older gentlemen play the mandolin.

Members who have just learned to play chord instruments like guitar or autoharp, derive much satisfaction from leading simple tunes which can be played with only the tonic and dominant seventh chords. Such songs include "Clementine," "Down in the Valley," "Everybody Loves Saturday Night," "He's Got the Whole World in His Hands," "Go Tell Aunt Rhody," "Oh! Woman," and many others. If a sufficient number of members can read braille, it is helpful to provide brailled song sheets.

Guitar, Ukelele and Folk Songs

The guitar, ukelele, and folk songs are usually included in one group activity, dependent upon the number of interested members and their abilities and capacities. Chords and strums are taught for accompaniment to folk and popular songs. There are no special adaptations. It is sometimes necessary to be tactual, i.e., have the members touch the finger positions of the teacher, or for the teacher to move and place the member's fingers on the strings in the proper fret.

Chords can be easily brailled over the lyrics where the chord changes, if the student can read braille.

Guitars and ukeleles for home practice are available at low cost. A good student guitar can be purchased for about twenty dollars. Procurement of musical instruments for blind members has been found to be a good service club project with a minimum of personal patronizing involvement. Members with some ability quickly learn to play several basic chords on the guitar or ukelele. They are then able to amuse themselves and others at home—and they proudly perform within the center. Members who continue to have difficulty with the simplest chords should be carefully transferred to the folk song group or to some other activity.

Figure 14. The recreation leader-guitar teacher kneels to manipulate the fingers of the member.

Rhythm Bands

It is an established recreation principle that all individuals should experience rhythm in some form. Rhythm bands are occasionally organized in recreation centers for older adults. However, this activity is too often associated with the play of younger children. Because blindness stereotypes imply dependency and childishness, the rhythm band does not seem to be a desirable music activity for blind adults.

Music Appreciation

Music appreciation is an activity akin to reading to blind persons. Unless the leader is knowledgeable and skillful, music appreciation becomes boring and drowsy listening. Planning, which begins at the member interest and comprehension level, with music supplemented by information about the composer and his intentions, are necessary elements of a good music appreciation activity. A

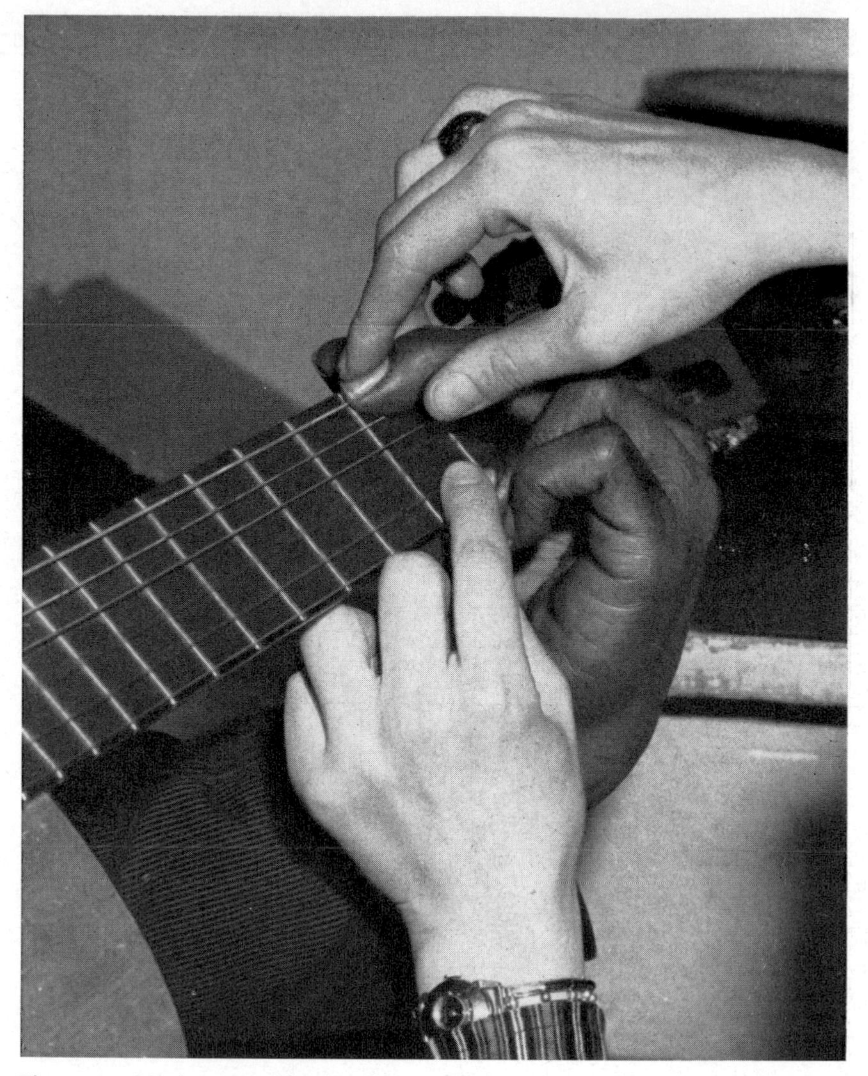

Figure 15. Much more effective than words, the guitar instructor is using both hands to position a member's fingers for an elementary "G" chord.

good record player is recommended so that the members may experience the quality of the music. Because the members cannot communicate with each other through their glances, more frequent interspersions with talk is helpful.

Neither facility nor equipment has to be specially adapted because of blindness. If a sufficient number of members are facile in braille, lyrics and chords can be brailled for individual study. Reasonable sound privacy is necessary for music appreciation, and again, practicing bands should not be where they will disturb other activities. Since blind persons should depend a great deal upon auditory experiences, the music and sound equipment ought to be of high quality.

Nature and Outings

An important recreation principle states that the specialized recreation center should plan its program in relation to the physical and cultural resources of the community, and make full use of such resources. Communities which are sufficiently sophisticated and resourceful to support specialized recreation centers are likely to include a wide array of educational and recreational opportunities for its citizens. The specialized recreation centers in New York City are fortunate in this respect. In every center, planful efforts are made to utilize the varied cultural community offerings, e.g., visits to the United Nations, museums, exhibits at the Coliseum, Rockefeller Center, parks and botanical gardens, opera, Circle Line trips around Manhattan Island, Hudson River Day Line outings and picnics, Staten Island Ferry trips, visits to wharfs and docked ships, and even visits to local community centers. One center features an annual weekend trip to Washington with an interesting itinerary of contacts within the nation's capital, including talks with Congressmen.

The immobility and isolation aspects of blindness, particularly as these relate to older folks, enormously enhance the positive significance of the preceding activities and experiences. Trips and outings are thrilling, educational, and engender enthusiasm for future planning, as well as stimulation and information for discussions.

There are problems, *viz.*, transportation arrangements and costs, ticket charges, adequate volunteer assistance in relation to size and make up of the member group, and public education and public relations considerations.

Members should generally be required to meet the cost of transportation if they are able to do so. It is occasionally possible to arrange for volunteer transportation because these are special re-

Figure 16. Curators are usually cooperative in making special arrangements for members to examine suitable objects by touch.

quests for non-recurrent service. It is also possible, sometimes, to get admission tickets free or at a discount. Again, if the member is able to pay, he should be asked to meet all or part of the actual cost. The ratio of required leadership assistance is dependent upon

Figure 16a. Totally blind student learning stern "J" stroke under watchful gaze of instructor. Position of instructor keeps center of gravity low for craft stability.

factors like the size of the group, the number of members without usable vision, the general adequacy of the members and of the available helpers, and the nature of the trip or outing. Generally, it is better, for public education purposes, to keep groups small, i.e., about ten to fifteen members. Larger groups are more likely to include blind individuals who too prominently affirm some of the negative blindness stereotypes. This is a constant probability because the members will be in unfamiliar surroundings. Some groping and helpless gesturing are almost inevitable; and so are patronizing reactions from the public.

Specialized recreation centers are often ancillary units of large multi-function rehabilitation agencies for the blind and/or the handicapped. Many such parent organizations own and operate at least one out-of-city facility which may be used to supplement the center recreation program. Some organizations have summer camps with comprehensive outdoor and indoor camping programs.

Figure 17. Younger adults relax at the juke box.

and canteen. Many centers provide lounges where a member can go and just sit, talk or watch television. The television set has a large screen, and chairs are arranged for close viewing without obstructing the view of other partially sighted members. Members who cannot see the screen enjoy listening and being part of the group. Most centers have some sort of canteen consisting of a variety of vending machines. Some centers include refreshment stands which dispense cans of beer, not always an unmitigated blessing.

Sports and Games

Many activities in this recreation category are included in specialized center programs. The most prominent and regularly recurrent activities follow:

1. Bingo
2. Bowling
3. Gymnastics
4. Pool (billiards)

5. Roller Skating
6. Table Games
7. Shuffleboard
8. Swimming

Several reasons are suggested for the widespread inclusion of sports and games activities, viz., the wide range of needed skills, efforts, and involvements, from the very simple in bingo to the very challenging in chess; from the relatively inactive in table games to the active in roller skating; and from mild rivalry in shuffleboard to intense competition in bowling. In the specialized recreation center for blind adults, most of whom tend to be over sixty years old, the concern for physical development is minimal, but there is a serious problem with the maintenance of physical vigor and prevention of physical debilitation.

Bingo

Bingo is a popular activity with most members, but it is especially desired by the older folks. Adapted bingo boards are available from the American Foundation for the Blind at about two dollars each. The boards are made of black plastic material with large white numbers in depressed squares in which the braille number equivalent appears. Therefore, a member can see the large white numbers if he has sufficient usable vision, or he may read the number with his fingers if he can read braille. Many members can do neither, and still do not wish to be left out ot the game. Various schemes have been devised to enable these members to play bingo independently, e.g., a board can be constructed so that the twenty-four numbers increase arithmetically by threes:

B	I	N	G	O
3	18	33	45	60
6	21	36	48	63
9	24	XX	51	66
12	27	39	54	69
15	30	42	57	72

Despite adaptation and contrivance, some members are able to play only if sighted volunteers check their boards for them. In some centers, arrangements are made for these members to sit at designated tables so that one volunteer can assist five or six individuals. Members should be urged to try to learn the first ten braille symbols and perhaps be able to play outside the center.

It is important to limit both the length of the activity and the prizes offered. In large programs, bingo ravenously uses quantities of donated prizes. Some centers charge five cents for a board, and the money collected is then returned in small prizes. The bingo caller, whether staff or member, should interject amusing commentaries, which help to make the game more interesting. Members who play independently are easily able to handle their own markers which are wooden squares just a shade smaller than the depressed squares on the bingo boards. Bingo can be played with small groups of about ten members, as well as with large groups of over one hundred members. Centers, in which social group work is the principal methodological commitment, tend to de-emphasize bingo despite its popularity with the members, because there is so little opportunity for constructive interpersonal involvements.

Bowling

Bowling is an activity of major proportions at many specialized centers. Some center facilities include regulation alleys which are fully used. Other centers make use of alleys located in community service clubs; or they use regular commercial alleys which are rented for practice, special events, and bowling tournaments.

The majority of active bowlers, particularly those in competitive leagues, tend to be men and women under fifty years of age. However, age is no real bar. In some programs, men and women in their seventies, and a few in their eighties, bowl regularly in noncompetitive or social bowling. In New York City, several hundred members bowl weekly at the center or on rented off-premises alleys. There are three formally organized competitive leagues for blind bowlers who are all affiliated with a national organization, The American Blind Bowlers Association. This organization conducts an annual national tournament, in a different city each season, in which more than six hundred blind bowlers compete for national championships, prize money, and trophies. The phenomenal growth of bowling for blind persons parallels a similar develop-

Figure 18. A totally blind bowler exhibits excellent form as he consistently knocks down wood for a 137 season average. A few totally blind bowlers occasionally break 200.

ment for the general population. In this sense, bowling has served as an admirable link with the community and with normality. Some of the better blind bowlers are accepted on regular bowling teams in their neighborhood, and some members regularly bowl socially with relatives and friends.

As a large muscle activity, bowling satisfies the severely deprived recreation need for activity and movement. Only minimum skill is required. Physical strength is a minor factor. Amiable rivalry and/or competitiveness makes bowling a significant means for promoting activity and movement within the center program. Bowling seems to appeal to both intellectual and non-intellectual members, men and women, young and old.

The only necessary adaptation is a fixed or portable guide rail, fifteen to twenty feet long and thirty-six inches high. This rail is used primarily by totally blind bowlers to determine direction straight down the alley, and the location of the foul line. The bowler without sufficient usable vision, after getting his ball, moves to the end of the guide rail which is at the foul line. He then steps back three, four, or five steps. On his approach delivery, the free hand glides lightly along the rail as he moves forward to the foul line to release the ball. Many totally blind bowlers prefer that the guide rails be in line with the inside edge of the alley gutters. This delimits the approach area so that it is easier for the blind bowler to orient himself and to aim the ball more accurately. However, handicapped bowlers with usable vision feel constrained by the narrowed approach area, and those who throw a hook ball find they cannot get their ball near enough to the edge of the alley. This is not too much of a problem with the portable rail on outside alleys.

Some handicapped bowlers cannot master the moving delivery. They bowl from a standing position at the foul line, i.e., at the end of the guide rail. Centers with bowling facilities usually have permanently fixed rails which run behind the gutters for right-handed and left-handed bowlers. Portable bowling rails can be purchased from the American Foundation for the Blind for approximately fifteen dollars.

Other bowling adaptations relate to optimum lighting for the bowlers with usable vision; and the recommendation that twin alleys with a center ball return are preferable to alleys with the return on one side. The center ball return reduces accident potential by eliminating the crossing of another alley to get a ball.

A sighted person, or member with sufficient vision, serves the essential function of identifying the pins remaining after the first thrown ball:

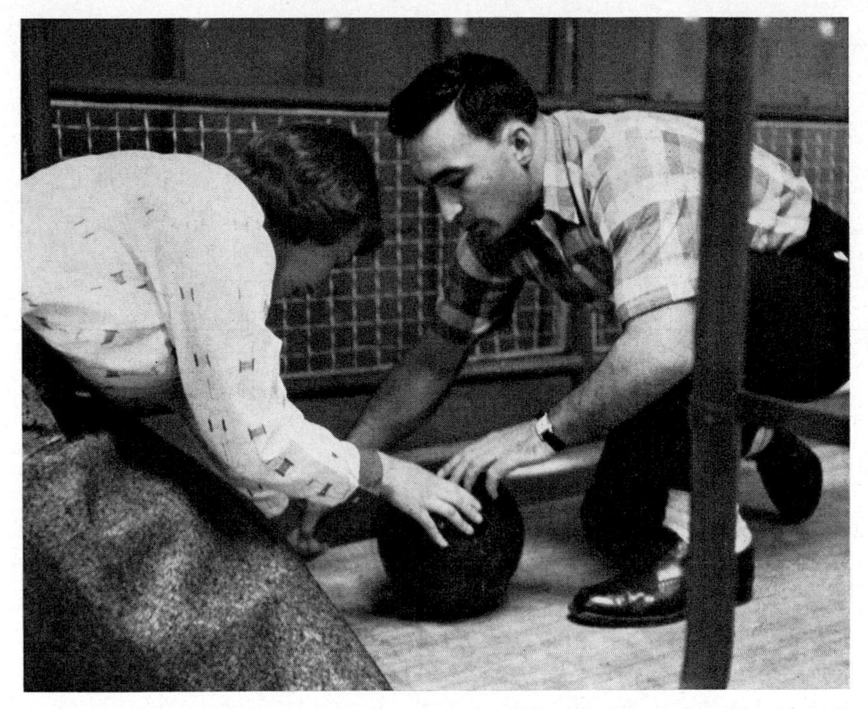

Figure 19. Bowling instructor is acquainting totally blind learner with the ball, its position upon release in relation to the finger holes and distance from the left gutter.

7 8 9 10
4 5 6
2 3
1

In many centers, the scorers are staff members who also function as activity leaders, instructors, and computers of competitive averages and team statistics. Provision for non-competitive and instruction bowling periods is a desirable practice. It is important to include light bowling ball, eight, ten or twelve pounders, for some of the non-competitive bowlers.

Sighted high school students serve admirably as pin-setters.

Figure 20. A former gym teacher, now blind, leads a group in mild simple calisthenics.

Usually it is necessary to pay them in order to insure continuity of the activity.

Gymnastics

Gymnastics should be a carefully circumscribed activity. Some specialized centers have small exercise rooms which are used by small groups of younger adults. Most members seem to know and are careful about their physical capacities in relation to vigorous exercise; but careful screening is advisable. Blindness is too often associated with other physical disabilities for which specific limitations are medically prescribed, e.g., certain eye conditions preclude vigorous bending, excessive vibration, or jumping. Exercise rooms usually contain a stationary bicycle (exercycle), rowing machine, wall weights and mats. The mats are used for lying-down exercises and some tumbling.

Knowledgeable and sensible supervision is extremely important.

This accounts, in part, for the fact that gym facilities are so little used in centers. However, there may be a sufficient number of younger adults, and some older members, who enjoy regular exercise, and who seem to benefit from the activity.

Pool Playing

Pool playing is very popular with male members who have enough usable vision to line up the cue ball, the object ball, and the pocket. Good lighting is helpful. In order to aim properly, some of the members have to play with their noses almost touching the green felt of the playing surface. Players are mostly younger men, under forty years of age. No special equipment adaptations are necessary. Cue tips need to be replaced relatively more often because visually handicapped players tend to lean the cue stick in an unbalanced position while waiting their turn to shoot. The seasonal replacement cost of the felt is about fifty dollars.

At some specialized centers, a variation of pocket pool known as bumper pool has become very popular. The playing surface is much smaller and therefore easier for the partially sighted person to encompass visually. Also, this piece of equipment can be purchased for about seventy-five dollars, whereas regular pool tables are much more expensive.

Roller Skating

Roller skating is an active, regularly recurrent activity in some centers. The participants are primarily younger men and women, under thrity, who have usable vision. In many centers, this once-popular activity has died out with the rise in membership age level. In a few centers, roller skating is handled as an outing or trip event. Special arrangements are made with a local roller rink to admit a group of blind members, each of whom is accompanied by a volunteer skating partner. Skating is fine exercise and the swift rhythmic movement meets many recreation needs and helps to overcome some of the intrinsic effects of blindness. For blinded members who skated when sighted, the activity can be a positive link with past skills and experiences.

In centers where roller skating is still popular with younger adults, caution is urged regarding necessary supervision and control. A high ratio of volunteer assistance is desirable. When someone falls it is imperative that help be immediately available, in order to avoid a pile up. Excessive speed should be censored quickly. No special adaptations are required. Regular indoor shoe skates with wooden or plastic wheels cost about fourteen dollars per pair. Some of the members bring their own skates. Usually, the center auditorium is used for skating. Both floor and skate maintenance present problems. Skating music provides rhythm and variety. It has proven desirable to have the music come from a specific localized point which can serve as a reference for the physical orientation of the skaters as they go around the auditorium rink.

Table Games

Table games attract many members, especially those with some facility with braille. Card games of various sorts are most popular. Members often organize themselves into regular groups, and become known as the poker club, pinochle club, bridge club and canasta club. Several kinds of rummy and lesser known card games like "chemin de fer" are also played in specialized center game rooms. Many centers permit nominal betting, which in poker parlance is known as "five and ten cent limit." It is desirable to make the card game just one of the activities in which the member participates, so that he has not come to the center just to play cards. For a good game, it is essential for the players without usable vision to read braille fluently. It is necessary to know only thirteen braille symbols in order to include the cards from ace to king, and the four card suits, clubs, diamonds, hearts and spades. In braille, the first ten alphabetic letters, "a" through "j" are identical with the numerals one through nine for the letter "i," with the tenth letter "j" being the zero numeral. A letter "c" is needed to designate the club suit; this is the numeral three. The letter "d," for diamonds, is the numeral four. The letter "j," for jack, is also used as the numeral zero to designate a ten. The three card identifications not covered by the first ten braille symbols are the letters "k" for king, "q" for queen, and "s" for the spade suit:

1	2	3	4	5	6	7	8	9	0
A	B	C	D	E	F	G	H	I	J
⠁	⠃	⠉	⠙	⠑	⠋	⠛	⠓	⠊	⠚

Figure 21. A quartet of four totally blind ladies are absorbed in gin-rummy while apparently awaiting the start of ceramics.

K	L	M	N	O	P	Q	R	S	T
⠅	⠇	⠍	⠝	⠕	⠏	⠟	⠗	⠎	⠞

The usual fan formation of holding the hand is difficult for a blind person though he may have played when sighted. Even in draw poker where only five cards are held, the small pack with the suits in some definite order, e.g., spades, hearts, diamond, clubs, has been found easiest. This is certainly the case when more cards are held as in gin-rummy, hearts, bridge and pinochle. Many efficient players, who play quickly, put each suit in order in a pack, then hold them in one hand, separating the suits with the fingers. The other hand keeps checking the brailled cards, somewhat like the seeing person who continually glances at his cards. Of course, if the player can see the cards, no differentiation is necessary though the cards may be brought to the nose and the game is slowed somewhat.

Figure 22. Adapted chess board and pegged chess pieces—black pieces are pointed or rounded; the white pieces have smooth flat tops.

It is advisable not to mix reasonably fast players with slow players, unless the game is conceived as a learning experience for the slow players—then the fast playing members see themselves as indigenous and patient volunteers.

Brailled cards can be purchased from the American Foundation for the Blind at about one dollar per pack. There are some organizations that give a deck of cards without charge to a blind person. Regular community bridge clubs are a good source for usable card deck solicitation. Brailling playing cards is a service offered by agencies fro the blind that have a braille transcribing service.

In chess, the pieces are shaped differently to identify opposing sides, i.e., the black chess pieces are ruffed on top, while the white pieces have smooth tops. The pieces are usually pegged to fit holes in the middle of the squares in the chess board. Some centers are experimenting with a chess board in which the alternate squares are depressed and the fitted chess pieces are identified by either a round or square base which fits into the depressed square. Not

Figure 22a. Standard adapted checker set. Note the small holes in one side which designates a King.

too many members play chess, but those who play are regulars. Occasional intra-center tournaments help to stimulate interest. Recently, a telephone and mail chess fraternity has developed among blind players living in different states and in Canada.

In the simpler game of checkers, the opposing twelve pieces are rounds and squares which fit into slightly depressed alternate positions on adapted checker boards. Each piece has a small center depression on one side which is turned upward when a king is made. A standard plywood or pressed-paper type board is available in stores which sell products made by blind persons, or from agencies for the blind.

A well-made plastic checker set is available without charge, from many local Lions Clubs. These sets are provided through Lions

Figure 23. Sturdy and light plastic checker set adapted for use by blind players; note depressed squares, round and square pieces, and the hollow side for Kings. White and black colors are helpful to sighted players.

International, 209 North Michigan Avenue, Chicago 1, Illinois. These checkerboards were provided through the courtesy of Dow Chemical Company and Wilson Plastics.

Adapted chess sets and wood or plastic checkerboard sets may be purchased from the American Foundation for the Blind at prices ranging from one to six dollars.

Dominoes is popular with older blind men and women. Domino pieces with raised pips from one through six are easily identifiable by players without vision, even if they cannot read braille. The simplest form of this matching game requires little or no leadership supervision. The more varied versions of dominoes attract some of the more intellectual members who need additional challenge in their game activities. Adapted domino games are also available from the American Foundation for the Blind for about two dollars per set.

Several language games, scrabble and anagrams, require not only sufficient braille reading ability, but also ability to remember and picture many word formations. Members with high school or higher education are more partial to scrabble and other language

Figure 24. Members review braille instructions and become familiar with domino pieces.

games. In scrabble, the pieces, white with black letters, are also brailled. The scrabble board squares are slightly depressed so that the pieces just fit into the squares to form the various words and word-combinations. These are the only adaptations. Scrabble games cost about seven dollars at the American Foundation for the Blind.

There are other table games in use at centers, but these are not used regularly, e.g., chinese checkers, monopoly, and variations of tic-tac-toe. The American Foundation for the Blind is the best source for the purchase of table games, as well as for advice and assistance with regard to necessary adaptations of regular games and materials.

Shuffleboard

Shuffleboard is played in many centers by small groups of two to four members. No special equipment adaptions are necessary. There are two types of board, *viz.*, a long board about twenty-eight feet in length, and a short board about twelve feet in length. The same pieces, four "A" weights, and four "B" weights are used to slide down the board to knock off the opposition weight and/or to score your own, by getting it as near as possible to the end of the board. Members without usable vision can play the game without leadership help, but more slowly. Players and/or leaders with usable vision help to accelerate the action and to add exciting descriptive content to the game. In some centers, shuffleboard has been developed into an important activity through the organization of tournaments and contests, with prizes and awards.

Maintenance of the shuffleboard's smooth surface is somewhat of a problem because some players throw rather than slide the weights. Weather and humidity are factors which have to be taken into account, for board surface maintenance. Boards should be cleaned, waxed, and sprinkled with wax powder quite often. The smaller shuffleboard costs approximately three hundred dollars. A set of eight weights is priced at thirty-two dollars. The long shuffleboard costs nearly one thousand dollars. Shuffleboards are manufactured by American Shuffleboard Company, Union City, New Jersey.

Swimming

Swimming is a regular program activity in only a few specialized centers which have their own swimming pools. Participation in swimming should be urged and promoted, because the activity is so tension-relieving, refreshing, and generally healthful. The buoyant effect of the water and the relaxing exercise counteract many intrinsic effects of blindness. There are many opportunities to relearn and/or perfect old skills, and to learn new ones. Six specific aquatic activities are included in specialized programs, *viz.*, (1) swimming and swimming skills; (2) life-saving and survival swimming skills; (3) diving; (4) skin diving; (5) water games, and (6) SCUBA diving.

Participants are usually younger men and women, but there may be some ladies and gentlemen in their sixties, and a few in their seventies. No special facilities adaptations are required. Physical movement outside the pool is necessarily slow and cautious. Medical clearance is essential, particularly in relation to certain eye

Figure 25. Jacques-Eves Cousteau, founder of SCUBA, expressed astonishment when he learned that totally blind persons were diving. A young totally blind college student is going down. A sighted buddy has already submerged.

conditions, e.g., high myopia and glaucoma. Recently there have been reports that individuals with certain allergies are adversely affected by chlorinated or brominated water commonly used in indoor pools. Usually, a somewhat elevated temperature is recommended because many visually handicapped swimmers do not move about as vigorously as sighted swimmers; and generally, blind persons simply are not in as robust physical condition as their sighted peers.

In many programs, the request for swimming is met by arranging for special swimming outings and classes in regular community center or commercial pools. Of course, this is generally desirable in relation to integration, i.e., public education and linking the blind person with non-segregated activities. However, there are some difficulties. The blind participants require almost one-to-one assistance in and around the locker rooms. There is serious concern on the part of pool management regarding increased insurance liability because of the realistic increase in accident potential, selected statistics notwithstanding. Proprietors of commercial pools worry about the effect on their sighted customers. Finally, the water and outside temperatures of many such pools are geared to the needs of the sighted.

Certain of the activities ordinarily would not be taught in a regular pool to a blind person, e.g., SCUBA diving. Younger blind adults have had an exciting and enriching experience in learning what it is really like to stay under water and be weightless in free-float. There are no words to describe the experience—and most blind persons live in a world of too many descriptions. Of course, no one expects a blind person to SCUBA regularly in outside waters. How many sighted do? But it is wonderful to really know what it is like under water, to hear strange sounds unknown elsewhere, and to propel oneself like a fish, with a relaxed kick of the finned feet. SCUBA diving is another link with a select group in the mainstream of living.

Sking diving, in which compressed air tanks and other paraphernalia are not needed, is a popular swimming activity at Camp Lighthouse in Waretown, New Jersey. This is a specialized camp for blind adults. Many come to camp with their own snorkels, fins and masks. Most persons who can swim can learn to skin-dive. The fact that one cannot enjoy the underwater sights does not negate the many other extrinsic values which derive from doing what is normal, what is admired. Intrinsically, it is very relaxing,

Figure 26. Totally blind college freshman-to-be has just gotten up on his skis on windless smooth Barnegat Bay, New Jersey.

and enjoyably different to swim about without having to lift your head to breathe.

Not only do blind individuals skin dive and SCUBA dive, some also water-ski.

Blind adult campers at Camp Lighthouse in New Jersey who can qualify by passing a basic swimming test developed by the local chapter of the American Red Cross may join the water-ski class. The group is led by a qualified life saver and water skier who uses the official teaching manual developed by the National Water Ski Association in Florida. In the past four seasons, thirty-one blind campers have been awarded their Elementary Water Ski cards and patches for their bathing suits. Every one of them proudly shows his emblem. Four have had the opportunity to water ski elsewhere, i.e., near their homes or while on vacation.

Figure 27. Totally blind college senior exhibits almost perfect water-skiing form on windy, wavy Barnegat Bay, New Jersey.

Miscellaneous Activities

Human activity which is in response to recreation need may be considered recreation. The intrinsic quality and/or quantity of an activity are relatively insignificant factors in their interpretation within a particular professional discipline, e.g., adult education, vocational training, adjustment, or recreation. The primary elements which identify an activity as recreation are the attitudes and motivations of the participants, and the evidenced satisfactions which are derived in the performance process. It is in this sense that a miscellany of non-categorized recreation activities may be included in the specialized recreation center programs:

1. Beauty Culture
2. First Aid
3. Home Nursing
4. Mobility
5. Ham Radio
6. Religious Activities
7. Tape Recording
8. Other

Beauty Culture

Beauty culture classes for women include hair cutting and styling, make-up and skin care, posture and good grooming, and weight control in relation to health and appearance. Of course, participant enthusiasm is enhanced by the derivative physical, psychological, and utilitarian benefits. The leaders, paid and volunteer, also get real satisfactions from their part in improving the outer, and perhaps the inner images of the members, who have so many real reasons for doubting themselves. There is no doubting the significant uplift experienced by a blind woman as a result of her new hairdo, facial, and some sincere fussing over her appearance by an interested worker. It is not difficult to obtain the cooperation of the beauty industry, e.g., volunteer consultants, hair cutters, and donations of beauty culture materials. Here is a recreation activity with positive transfer values in which the image of blindness is altered constructively, member by member. Perhaps this is why beauty culture volunteers are reported to be such dependable leaders.

First Aid and Home Nursing

First aid and home nursing are taught by qualified instructors assigned by the local Red Cross chapters. Where these classes have been included in center programs, they have been full to capacity. The usual abundance of patience and some simple ingenuity in adapting procedures and equipment make these useful skills achievable for the members. These classes demonstrate the interest and the concern of the members for themselves and others. Such activities also serve as additional links from the community to the center and to the members. Satisfactory completion of the course means the awarding of official Red Cross certificates. This is tangible recognition of meaningful accomplishment for the community, the Red Cross, the center, the leaders, and, of course most of all, the blind individuals.

Mobility (indoors)

Mobility, in this category, refers to movement within the center. Particularly in larger centers where there are more than one hundred members in a season, it is imperative and desirable that planful efforts be made to teach and encourage independent movement between rooms and floors of the facility. Here is a prime area for the positive utilization of indigenous leadership. Members are eager to serve on welcoming committees, and on individual orientation assignments. Both parties are encouraged and strengthened in this mutual interaction, particularly if the orientor happens to be a mobile totally blind member.

In some situations, it is necessary to use staff, paid or volunteer, to planfully improve the mobility of certain members. Often, mobility practice is combined with required fire drills. Sometimes it is helpful to organize exploration trips around the center and/or the entire agency building. One of the best motivations for independent member movement is related to the pervading attitude of offering assistance only when it is needed and wanted, thus impelling members to move without help.

Ham Radio

Ham radio operation might be included in the "Language Category" as a communications activity. However, sending and/or receiving messages is preceded by an extended period of learning about electronics. In addition, each member is required to construct an elementary receiving set, from a kit—and then comes the wonderful reward of an official license as a ham operator. In one center, a group of members with special skills and interests have organized themselves as a Ham Radio Club. They have an extensively equipped club room and are immensely proud of their registered call letters. In another center, a more elementary group is led by a volunteer who is a science high school teacher. He provides most of the equipment, some of which is on official loan from his school. Members who can afford it purchase their own receiving kits and supplies. Many interpersonal and community connections can be forged through this recreation activity.

Religious Activities

Religious activities need to be carefully circumscribed. Blindness seems to have little partiality with respect to religious persuasion, although in the New York City centers, a slight predominance of Roman Catholics is discernible. This is probably an

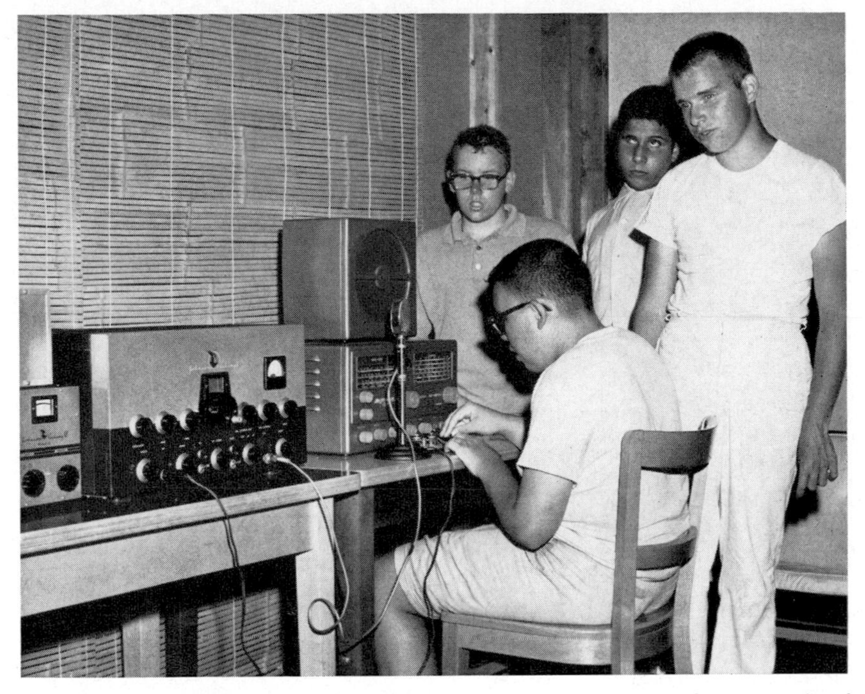

Figure 28. Licensed ham, totally blind, is teaching teenagers the fundamentals of receiving, sending and code. His set includes adapters for aural tuning.

associational phenomenon with demographic and geographic factors accounting for this larger religious prevalence. An aggressive attempt should be made to handle religious differences in a positive and constructive manner. Frank and open attitudes of acceptance and respect for all religions should be fostered through discussion groups and joint participation in religious festivals and ceremonials to the extent that this is permitted by particular religious tenets. Adherences to religious obligations should be encouraged, and the proscribed eating of meat on Friday should be officially observed in serving food and refreshments.

Mindful of the fact that so many members are elderly, some centers have instituted monthly memorial ceremonies which seem to please a great many members. Another monthly ceremonial recognizes birthdays which serves to individualize as well as bind members together in common humanness. In centers with large numbers of non-white and/or Puerto Rican members, similar efforts should be made to emphasize the positive aspects of human differences. The intrinsic and extrinsic effects of blindness, common to all the members, tend to ameliorate somewhat the fears and prejudices held by particular members who, on the whole, possess less knowledgeable and less sophisticated attitudes toward racial, religious and nationality minorities.

Unfortunately, it is evident that neither common misfortune nor common denegation, nor propinquity can be relied upon to engender understanding and acceptance. Nonetheless, the planful integrative activities, conducted in the pervasive atmosphere of satisfactions derived from meeting recreation needs, seem to reassure and relax the tensions and defenses which separate people.

Tape Recording Clubs

Tape recorded groups are a recent development. Many blind persons already are familiar with the Talking Book, the phonograph for which all legally blind individuals are eligible through request to their local or state, public or voluntary agency for the blind. Members enjoy learning how to operate the various types of tape recorders. Some of the members can talk expertly about the special advantages of certain recorders and tapes. It is apparent that this skill and knowledge significantly contributes to self-satisfaction and self-confidence. Tapes can be used in a more flexible and more personal manner than Talking Book records. Some members are already in exchange correspondence, via tape, with individuals in other states; and some members have exchanged tape recordings with contacts in Europe.

Tape club members can use their equipment to record special center programs, which they do with enthusiasm and effectiveness. They also assist the center drama groups by recording individual scripts and recitations, as well as by taping needed sound effects. The Tape Club can also develop various tapes for use in dance classes, and record practice sessions of some of the center bands. Tape recording is another center activity which can function well with adequate member leadership. One of the mundane objectives of the tape groups is the possession of at least one home tape recorder by each member. Many interesting and worthwhile group projects can be initiated by the members to achieve this desirable goal. Community service clubs and local electronics stores and factories are quite willing to cooperate through donations of recorders, tapes, and sometimes funds. Such special interest solicitations should be carefully controlled, but these materialistic goals add to the vigor and viability of the groups.

Other

Recreation workers should be alert for varied activities which constructively meet the needs, interests and capacities of the registrants. However, there should always be awareness of the negative factors involved in promoting activities in which good visual perception is essential for successful performance. The inherent need to deny reality, by participants and staff alike, can lead to contrivance or gimmickry which engenders doubt and anxiety and invokes anew the ghosts of wonder and pity.

Knowledgeable recreation workers planfully seek and select activities in accord with professional principles, and not to demonstrate that blindness may perhaps be a mere nuisance, for some people. There are many desirable special activities, e.g., (1) gardening in porch boxes for individuals who enjoy growing things, who like the odor and texture of flowers and who want to learn to identify common flowers like tulips, hyacinths, jonquils and roses; (2) the making of artificial flowers with wires and scrap materials; (3) courses in memory and concentration which are useful skills when one is blind; (4) brainstorming sessions which encourage people to express their ideas, and to hitchhike on the ideas of others without fear of contradiction and ridicule, often a real catharsis, and many others.

There are also many reasonably priced commercial games which can readily be adapted for use with little or no sighted assistance—a desirable objective, e.g., bowl-ball in which a four-inch wooden ball is rolled toward a target that consists of numbered paddles which are turned up for a score when struck by the ball. The paddles are easily brailled by using round-head tacks. Knok-Hockey is another commercial game that is popular with younger and older adults and requires no adaptation. Both games are manufactured by Carron Industries, Inc., Luddington, Michigan.

A plethora of activities, is no guarantee of program superiority

Figure 29. Knok-Hockey is inexpensive game equipment which can be used independently by players without usable vision.

or even adequacy. People-centered programs are designed with a consideration for time as an unhurried dimension which enables members to talk, philosophize, compliment, reprimand, and sympathize—time for each other as well as for the completion of specific, tangible projects.

Whether the specialized recreation program is ancillary to the rehabilitation function of a larger agency, or whether the specialized recreation program operates as a single organization, the constructive integration of invaluable diagnostic data so readily available from purposeful observation of member behavior in program activities is a professional obligation, particularly in the leisure-time informal education-based centers. It is presumed that such information will be noted and used for the benefit of members in both social group work and recreation education oriented programs.

Chapter VI

LEADERSHIP

Paid Staff

PHILOSOPHY, principles, objectives, auspices, activities, site and facilities, equipment and materials are all program elements which are integrated by administration to function in well-defined or in confused patterns of relationships through which an organization moves, with sureness or with uncertainty, in the direction of its avowed goals. Perhaps, the organization does not move at all, except backwards, because knowledge and values regarding individuals and communities are continually changing.

Obviously, all program factors affect total center performance, but the relevant significance of each factor is determined in large measure by leadership. It is quite clear that all other program factors are subservient to leadership. The solid, the valid accomplishments of the specialized recreation service are a direct function of the quality of the leadership involved in the operation of the program.

Leadership Qualifications

To cope successfully with the unique problems of the blind individuals who need specialized services, staff should possess at least the basic competencies required for similar work with the non-handicapped. This has been a basic assumption throughout this book. Certainly all recreation leaders should have an excess supply of patience. The recreation worker in the specialized center needs inexhaustible patience, as well as a concurrent ability to consciously slow his working tempo.

Too often, one hears the exclamation, "they are so happy!" Perhaps this is the natural and protective reaction to the fear and gloom expectation of the average lay observant. Perhaps this conception has some deeper validity. Nonetheless, the specialized worker needs an extra-good sense of humor as well as a hopeful enthusiasm that reaches out to individuals whose defenses against despair are uncertain and weak.

There should be familiarity with the history and development of "work for the blind," or "services to blind individuals," which is a more positive and suggestive reference. Because relationships tend to be friendlier and easier in the recreation setting, leaders should be able to discuss knowledgeably the current trends in the field, not as experts, but just as interested citizens. Specialized workers ought to know something about prevalent eye conditions and their implications for member participation in center program activities. The identified effects of blindness, intrinsic and extrinsic, are certainly essential data for all specialized program staff. A specialized center leader with a working knowledge of braille has increased effectiveness. The staff member who makes the effort to learn the manual alphabet in order to more quickly communicate with the occasional trained deaf-blind member, is looked upon with awe, admiration and a little envy. Like regular qualified recreation and/or group workers, specialized workers are more effective if they have skill competence in some or many specific program activities in addition to being excellent conversationalists.

As professionals, staff members should know, understand, and accept the purposes and aims of the center. However, this need not imply agreement with the operational methods utilized to achieve program goals. Social science theories and concepts are still largely hypothetical, and human dynamics are pragmatically interpreted through many formulations and directed toward the ideal goals contained in the conceptualization of American Democracy.

Remuneration

It is a curious paradox that in "service for blind individuals," a field of work especially favored by legislation, in literature, through the existence of hundreds of specialized community agencies, and through other forms of social concerns, recruitment of staff is difficult. Retention of specialized staff on the supervisory and leadership levels is even more difficult. Many current staff members, in these latter classifications, are lacking in professional and other basic qualifications.

Recent American Foundation for the Blind studies reveal that specialized supervisory and leadership salaries are approximately 20 per cent below the prevalent minimums for qualified regular recreation or group workers. Annual salaries for supervisors in specialized centers range from approximately $4,000 to $7,000. Leadership salaries begin as low as $3,500 and go to $5,000. Of course, administration must include copious quantities of "dedication," a noble sentiment but a poor substitute for genuine professional concern and competence.

To make matters worse, little time and leave recognition is given to the exceptional strain on staff in direct contact with the handicapped members. There is an unrealistic tendency to assume that in the recreation setting everyone is having fun. No wonder that staff possessing professional and technical qualifications are soon attracted to other fields. However, some qualified workers are challenged to remain. They are determined to establish recreation or group work as a priority service which actually has wide community sanction because the specialized center is the most effective institution in which to meet the recreation needs of large numbers of isolated and debilitated blind persons.

Regular and specialized recreation centers have to employ relatively large numbers of part-time workers. Hourly wage rates range from $1.50 to $5.00 per hour, dependent upon the specific skills and qualifications of the worker, e.g., pin-setters or bowling scorers earn $1.50 per hour whereas a ceramics, dance or drama leader may get $5.00 per hour. Locale and work hours also affect salary rates.

If leadership is the "*sine qua non*" of program, staff quality and staff morale should be primary concerns of administrative power. Experience suggests that it is often wiser not to offer a service at all (as cruel as this sounds) than to venture into programs with inadequate leadership resources. A beacon of hope has appeared on the horizon. The American Foundation for the Blind has sponsored a Commission on Standards and Accreditations of Service for the Blind. Because recreation is one of the most frequently rendered services to blind persons, there can be little doubt that the established evaluative criteria will result in an upgrading of those educational and social service programs which merit accreditation.

Volunteer Workers

The specialized recreation center and the parent organization are positive expressions of citizen interest, concern, responsibility and sanction. There is general recognition that voluntary service is a fundamental characteristic of American social democracy. Edward C. Lindeman, teacher, social scientist, and philosopher, wrote that the volunteer continues faithfully to make his contribution of time, devotion, and money not because of any legal compulsion, but because of "obedience to the unenforceable"[1] A similar notion was expressed in *The Royal Bank of Canada Monthly Letter*:

> One does not need to have a romantically heightened view of giving oneself away, but only to remember that the contribution made by individuals and groups voluntarily is the real foundation of democratic society, and that it is one of the ways in which, in spite of mechanization and automation, we remain human.[2]

The faithful volunteer has been virtually the life blood of the specialized recreation center program. With program activities so heavily weighted with handcrafts, and with the participants totally blind or severely visually handicapped, the required degree of individual assistance has not been feasible in any other way. Many activities in the recreation categories of dance, drama, games and music require a ratio of membership to leadership which can be approximated only through the utilization of volunteer assistants. The volunteer is an essential program resource. The fact is that three of every five staff members in existent centers are unpaid. In many centers, only the overall supervisor or director is a paid worker.

[1]Quoted in Brooklyn Bureau of Social Service and Children's Aid Society, "Teamwork for Community Service," *92nd Annual Report*, June, 1958.

[2]The Royal Bank of Canada: The volunteer in our society, *The Royal Bank of Canada Monthly Letter*, *XLIII*, No. 8, Montreal, Canada, August, 1962.

Volunteers of widely different training, experience, ability, interest and motivation serve in many capacities, viz.: as formal advisory and policy-making representatives of community interest and concern (board member); as interested and knowledgeable fund raisers and procurers of equipment, materials, and other volunteers; as skilled leaders to impart their skills, knowledge and attitudes, or as assistants leaders who perform the indispensable tasks of preparing materials, equipment, refreshments, or act as readers, guides, or just listeners. Others help in a myriad of unclassified but necessary supportive tasks which are beyond the attention and capacitites of paid staff. They may act as personal and informed public emissaries who help to link the center with the community and to project a positive public image of blind individuals and the center as a whole. They may also be enthusiastic conveyors of ideas and suggestions which enrich the program.

Carefully selected and properly supervised volunteers can significantly promote a center atmosphere which helps to sustain visually handicapped persons with a respect for their individual dignity and their individual capacity to take responsibility for themselves. This must be the real intent and meaning of the shop worn cliché slogan "help the blind to help themselves." In such a milieu, blind persons can be helped to find satisfaction instead of misery, achievement instead of failure, and recreation activity instead of debilitating indolence. In this setting, deep-rooted tenacious blindness stereotypes may continually be weakened thus strengthening the members and the community, enlightening both.

The obvious importance of volunteers requires extensive delineation of the areas associated with their utilization.

Recruitment

Volunteers are a direct function of the public image of an institution. Volunteers may be obtained through formal publicity in the mass communication media, e.g., radio, television, newspapers, and magazines. Direct contacts with local community organizations and service clubs are often fruitful sources. Student service groups in regular high schools, or youngsters from vocational high schools, make excellent activity assistants, guides, and refreshment and meal servers. Undergraduate and graduate students in education, sociology and psychology can be recruited as field work students. The bond with local colleges and universities is particularly fortunate, because these institutions of higher learning also serve as sources for speakers. They may also provide technical assistance in research, evaluation, and staff improvement.

Often, volunteers beget other volunteers—relatives and friends. Sometimes a center member brings in a resourceful relative or friend who is eager to be of some assistance—but away from the member-recruiter, unless the particular member is deaf-blind, spastic-blind, or temporarily so immobilized with fear and uncertainty as to require one-to-one companionship and assistance. Recently, a new productive resource for volunteers has appeared, the retired individual anxious to be occupied meaningfully. Senior citizen groups, retired teacher associations, university alumni groups, community councils, unions and chambers of commerce are sources for recruiting the retired individual. Obviously, such volunteers bring a wealth of experience, skills and understanding, as well as ingrained attitudes toward dependency and blindness.

Screening

Supervisors deplore the too oft reality that need for human assistance leads to rationalized acceptance or retention of volunteers who quite obviously will be minimally effective in carrying out their assignments. Most centers have experienced volunteers with personal needs and attitudes which actually deprive the members of opportunities for expression and achievement. These self-centered, troubled helpers perpetuate and strengthen the blindness stereotype, dependence-superiority. In either case, they are destructively righteous because the member's dignity is lowered as well as his capacity for self-expression.

Screening of volunteers should occur on the supervisory level. Emotional stability and motivation for wishing to help blind persons must be ascertained. Sufficient data should be gleaned to make initial judgments about the general attitudes and skills of the prospective volunteer. Particularly important are attitudes about differences in people, i.e., differences in physique, race, creed, national origin, education, socio-economic levels, mental and behavior idiosyncrasies and, of course, visual deprivation. Lately, volunteer-screening interviewers have sensitively inserted an inquiry regarding psychotherapy experience, because of subsequent difficulties.

A note of caution must be sounded here. Professional staff should guard against a tendency to deprecate demonstrated sympathy for hurt humanity. Altruistic sentiments are respectable, whether they arise from one's identification with blind persons, a guilty conscience, penance for personal sins, or a desire to appear noble and self-sacrificing. Whatever the complete combination of motives, the common impulse to do for others should not be inquired into so closely that suspicion and doubt quench its existence. Many persons have little conscious understanding of why they are volunteering. They become upset by questions which seem to cast doubt on their intentions.

There undoubtedly are and probably will continue to be volunteers who simply are unable to accept, intellectually and/or emotionally, the principles of self-determination and self-help for the members. Volunteers who demonstrate such stubborn inability should be encouraged to exploit their interests, talents and energies in center tasks which involve only minimal personal contact with members. However, there are times when it is necessary to administratively terminate the relationship with a volunteer, after the initial interview or after a period of service. To be constructive, the supervisor should be courteous, dignified, explicit and, if possible, have some alternative suggestions, perhaps directing the volunteer into areas which involve no contact with deprived individuals. Most useful is the availability of written materials which include information about the selection, training, supervision and evaluation of volunteers. There should be provision for a probation period during which the volunteer or the center may decide whether the best interests of both will be served by continuance, reassignment or termination.

The screening interview should also attempt to determine the volunteer's dependability in relation to regularity of attendance and punctuality; willingness to accept training and supervision and, as with all specialized workers, an apparent abundance of patience buttressed with a sense of humor.

Training

New volunteers are usually eager for immediate assignments, as if to prove to themselves and others how useful they can be; and most programs urgently need volunteers. Supervisors should insist on prior-to-assignment orientation sessions. These classes may be conducted monthly or bi-monthly. Pre-assignment orientation should include familiarization with the physical aspects of the center and the parent agency, introduction to key staff who have some relationship to the recreation function, lectures and discussions about the program, instructional meetings with skill workers, and then intern-type assignments under supervision. In-service training should continue through staff meetings, conferences and exposure to appropriate writings in the field.

Direct service volunteers may be occasional assistants who come in for special program events only. They may be regularly assigned leaders and helpers who come in once a week or oftener for activities which are on-going all season, or for a specific activity project like a home nursing or first aid course. Experience suggests caution when a volunteer wishes to devote too much time to "the blind." Abstractly, dedication is a fine sentiment, but like the road to hell, it is fraught with peril for all in direct services. Too often, the personal needs of such volunteers results in intrusion into serious member problems which should be handled only by the professional staff.

Concern about the deleterious effects of such volunteer involvements led an authority in the field to suggest the requirement of a formal pledge of restricted activity:

> I pledge myself to be the eyes of the blind. I will try with all that lies within me to be free of false feelings about blindness—feelings that blind persons are strange or different—feelings that they have a sixth sense or miraculous compensation—feelings that they are geniuses or that, on the other hand, they have warped or twisted personalities.
>
> I will attempt to realize completely what I am now beginning to recognize, that there is no common personality pattern among

> blind persons. And I will try always to see each individual blind person with whom I come in contact as an individual human person with an individual human personality.
>
> . . . .
>
> And my actual relationship to the person to whom I am assigned will be the relationship which is assigned to me . . . I will refrain from any attempt to influence the life or actions of the person who is blind—I will not try to be mother or father or sister or brother to the person who is blind. I will not allow myself to be financial benefactor to him. Nor will I own or possess him. I will not make him dependent on me—nor myself dependent on him.[3]

Such brusqueness is understandable to those who have labored with this problem. Perhaps the angry proponent of the pledge is a little harsh on those who are trying to give of themselves. Abhorrence of severe physical aberration, of death, and, yes, of blindness seems to be a universal factor in human behavior. Many of us can work out this fundamental fear so that we can be genuinely helpful. To require a volunteer to report all unassigned tasks assumed in relation to a member, with adequate explanation and interpretation of this dictum in training and supervising, should suffice to safeguard the member and the volunteer.

Pledges have not been notably successful in ordering desirable attitudes or conduct. Remember that to many members, a volunteer possesses a special quality of personal relationship by virtue of being an unpaid worker. Volunteers can often develop a more positive member relationship than the professional worker. It is essential that volunteers understand and accept the fact that no dichotomy can exist between the best interests of the member and the program. The volunteer who is able to develop a warm trusting relationship with a member is in a unique position to help the professional work to help the member.

Supervision

Volunteers are staff members and their supervision should be considered within this frame of reference. Supervisory methods should include planned individual and group conferences in which

[3]Carroll, *op. cit.*, pp. 357-358.

individual performance and problems are discussed as well as general observations and concepts. Volunteers should be included in staff meetings which deal with activity program content, the achievement of center goals, and the discussion of member problems. In this latter connection, diagnostic observations should be emphasized as a function of recreation leadership, e.g., how to recognize and how to encourage an overly dependent member to move in the direction of self-help; how to give support to an insecure member so he can risk himself in moving about and trying new activities and associations; how to gently but firmly set limits which will help to impart a little patience in a member who cannot wait; how to use humor in dealing with a member's anger and irascibility in terms of what these emotions may signify; how to increase social awareness and conversation ability in the isolated individual as well as perhaps when and why to leave a member alone for a while. There are so many fruitful areas of human conduct to examine with volunteers in order that their understanding of the members, themselves and the objectives of the program become clearer and more meaningful. Reading and discussion of recreation literature should be made readily available. Attendance at appropriate recreation meetings, councils, conventions should be encouraged.

Time requirements in activities, in training workshops, in individual and group conferences should be explicitly planned and specified. A record should be kept of attendance regularity and punctuality. Most volunteers like to sign in. It should be clearly understood that the activity leader is responsible for all the volunteer assistants in the activity, even though conference supervision may derive from a supervisor of volunteers.

Evaluation

Evaluation is a continuous process and a function of on-going supervision. The individual supervisory conference is essentially a method for increasing the volunteer's self-awareness and knowledge, in relation to his performance as a worker. Written materials in recreation are replete with suggestions which enable a worker to examine more objectively his efforts in behalf of the members and the center. For example, the Recreation Commission of the City of Long Beach, California, has developed an interesting self-evaluation questionnaire titled, "How'm I Doing-Chart."[4] While intended primarily for professional recreators in regular settings, many of the areas covered are pertinent to the functions of volunteers, particularly because they predominate quantitatively in the specialized programs. "How'm I Doing-Chart" includes six major sections:

1. Professional Preparation and Outlook
2. Personal
3. Human Relations
4. Program
5. Organization
6. Equipment, Supplies, Facilities, Areas and Buildings

Each section contains from twelve to twenty simply-worded queries which direct the practitioner's attention to an evaluation of his concerns and activities in the particular area. For example, in Section (1), Professional Preparation and Outlook, the first question is, "Have I taken advantage of formal education opportunities in colleges, universities, and/or adult education centers to the extent that I feel secure in meeting the challenges and problems of my position?" The content of this question can be easily adapted so that its intent is valid and meaningful for the specialized center volunteer. Another question, "Have I read a new recreation book within the past year?" needs little or no change. Perhaps, a specialized center supervisor might want to have the question contain a more specific reference to *Recreation Magazine* or *The New Outlook for the Blind.*

In Section (2), Personal, the second question "Am I in sympathy with the recognized objectives of the recreation program?" contains enough self-evaluative thought-provoking content for the worker as well as for the supervisor. The obvious assumption is that the volunteer is familiar with the specified objectives of the program. There is also the fundamental assumption that the center has explicitly specified these objectives. Would that this was always the case.

[4]City of Long Beach, California Recreation Commission: "How'm I Doing-Chart" for Recreation Play Directors, July 18, 1955 (mimeo).

The third section, Human Relations, is full of searching questions like number (8), "Am I understanding and tolerant when confronted with human problems brought about as a result of personal anxieties, misunderstandings and limitations on the part of associates and/or patrons?"

Section (4), Program, poses question (13), "Do I have an effective plan in operation which assures the underprivileged or less capable patron of getting a fair share of my time, energy and attention?"

Section (5), Organization, includes a wide range of questions concerned with administrative matters which are directly applicable to programs where volunteers serve as supervisors and managers, e.g., Question (9), "Do I have an effective and democratic organization for bringing proper social pressures to bear upon those whose language or attitudes and/or actions need correction?"

Section (6), Equipment, Supplies, Facilities, Areas and Facilities is concerned with adequacy for program activities, housekeeping, safety and appearance, e.g., Question (7) "Are the supplies and equipment stored in an oderly and efficient way so patron may check them out quickly when desired?" Responsible recreation center practitioners know the importance of a well-ordered systematic handling of supplies and equipment. In the specialized recreation center for blind persons, such a question has relevance in terms of mobility, independence and responsibility.

Altogether, the "How'm I Doing-Chart" contains ninety-three searching questions which can serve as a font for worker and supervisor in their evaluative efforts to improve the quality of their performance and thus the quality of service.

The act of pausing to take stock, to contemplate performance and accomplishment is inherently constructive and satisfying. From the administrative view, the evaluative process is not only educational and strengthening for the volunteer worker, but also essential for the supervisory determination of the worker's effectiveness. How else can the supervisor judge dependability; adaptability; workmanlike approach to tasks; willingness to accept the center's philosophy and objectives, policies and methods; response to supervision and criticism? How better can we help to develop and improve the quality of staff efforts? Evaluation is the core ingredient of supervision.

Recognition

As man is predominately a social animal, recognition must rank as a primary basic human need. It is intimately associated with such other basic needs as achievement and affiliation.

When asked their reasons for volunteering, many applicants are taken aback and respond hesitantly while apparently searching for their conscious motives. One can sense deeper meanings beneath the articulated reasons. Therefore, subsequent satisfactions are more likely to be in the realm of intangibles. How tangible is the experience when a member graciously expresses appreciation, a reward which the volunteer has neither sought nor expected. Real enough is the quality of joy known only to those *amicus humani generis* who give of themselves for others.

Nevertheless, esoteric satisfactions are significantly enhanced through planful and more tangible acknowledgments of special accomplishments and services. One of the most effective methods, conceptually simple but pragmatically difficult, is recognition through timely praise by the supervisory leaders—simply expressed and for genuine effort and skillful accomplishment. Annual meetings, end-of-season parties, staff dinners, and recreation exhibits can serve as events in which volunteers may participate and be recognized and rewarded. Well-designed certificates, scrolls and service pins should be ceremoniously awarded for meritorious service, while the indispensability of all volunteers is proclaimed as a solid reality. Selected volunteers should be named and written up in the organizational literature. They should also be included often in the press releases to local news media. Volunteers should receive agency news bulletins, informationals, annual reports and invitations to special events.

Summary

The volunteer is vital to the operation of the specialized recreation center for blind persons. The specialized program rests upon the assumption that the members cannot have their recreation needs met through regular community services. The volunteers therefore serve as effective links to the mainstream of living from which handicapped individuals should not be separated. Of course, volunteers serve practically as necessary leaders, supervisors and administrators.

Recruitment, selection, training, supervision, evaluation and recognition are interrelated aspects of a continuous process of growth and development for volunteers as well as for paid staff. Volunteers should be viewed in this context. It may sometimes become necessary to terminate the center relationship with a volunteer. Just as with any staff worker, frank and dignified discussion will safeguard the interests of all concerned. In this connection, experience suggests concern, when any volunteer devotes too much time to "the blind." In a general sense, dedication is a fine sentiment, but it is fraught with peril on the direct service level. Too often, the personal needs of these volunteers result in disturbing personal involvements with members within and outside of the center. Leaders and supervisors should be wary of compromising rationalizations based on program or other expediencies—even when an ineffective volunteer suggests a resultant change in legacy.

Professions

In 1964, at long last, a national effort culminated in the establishment of professional criteria for the accreditation of Recreators, *viz.*,

1. Baccalaureate degree with a major in recreation; and 500 hours of satisfactory experience in recreation service; or
2. Baccalaureate degree with a major in a recreation-related field and a total of twelve months of satisfactory career experience in recreation service, or
3. Baccalaureate degree and twenty-four months of career experience in recreation service.

College transcripts and employer statements are required. Like the A.M.A., for doctors of medicine, and the A.C.S.W., for social workers, the accreditating organization is made up of prominent and authoritative recreation educators and practitioners and is known as The American Recreation Society, Inc., 1404 New York Avenue, N.W., Washington, 5, D.C. Communities have become increasingly aware of the fact that organized recreation is a valuable social institution through which urbanized man can constructively meet many of his basic needs. Considerable data are available regarding recreation principles, purposes, programs, and leadership. This knowledge has been delineated and classified in many colleges and universities where a student majoring in recreation may earn an undergraduate, a master's and even a doctor's degree.

Another requirement for professional status is the development of firm methodologies of performances for the achievement of the specified aims and objectives. Recreation as a profession seems to be weak precisely because of a failure to clarify its methodologies and relate them more specifically to its avowed goals and objectives. We must do better than reiterate that recreation constructively meets the needs of individuals. There should be greater inquiry into the benefits and values derived from participation in particular recreation activities as well as firmer knowledge regarding the various methods of conducting particular activities.

The center and the worker have an obvious stake in professional growth and development. Both should take positive and explicit responsibility for providing the climate, the time, and the resources which will promote self-satisfying improvements in staff competencies. The center should provide the means through which staff members, particularly those on the leader levels, may secure additional training via in-service programs, as a regular part of center work schedules. Appropriate time off should be arranged for workers to attend selected training sources given by colleges, groups of agencies, or other training sources. The centers should maintain a staff library stocked with pertinent standard and current professional writings, and promote frequent use of these materials through regular forums and meetings.

Staff should be continually alert to developments in the social science professions that may result in changes in methods and materials which enhance member participation and achievement. With the encouragement and cooperation of center administration, all staff members should be active in some of the professional and service recreation and social group work organizations, viz.: the American Recreation Society, the National Recreation Association, the National Association of Social Workers, and the American Association of Workers for the Blind. Center workers should regularly read the periodicals published by these organizations, e.g., *The American Recreation Journal*, *Recreation Magazine*, *Social Work*, and *Proceedings* of the annual A.A.W.B. conventions. Attendance and active participation in the meetings and conventions of these professional and service organizations should be facilitated. Appropriate recognition should be given to members who devote their time and talents to the expansion of knowledge in the field.

In this connection, staff should be familiar with the library and other research facilities and services of the American Foundation for the Blind. Workers should be urged to be research minded as a means for doing a more effective job as well as for personal growth and development. The humanitarian professions cannot be practiced in a vacuum. Professional workers need to frequently renew and evaluate their purposes and goals, knowledge and practices, in order to work most effectively in a field in which understanding and values are changing.

Chapter VII

ADMINISTRATION

ADMINISTRATION encompasses planning, organizing, managing, directing, controlling and evaluating the specialized recreation center. These processes occur to a greater or lesser extent on all levels of leadership function. For example, an arts and crafts instructor plans the activity of the class, organizes the resources available and manages these resources in relation to the members. The instructor also directs the members and the helpers, and controls and evaluates the activity and the accomplishments.

As one goes up the scale in the administrative hierarchy, the managerial factors increase. There is more concern with overall aspects of administrative effectiveness in relation to the philosophy and objectives of the center. Administration thus encompasses many means to many ends. Proper administration, like leadership, can get the most from whatever center resources are available. However, improper administration can result in the pauperization of recreation opportunities and experiences, in superior settings, with the most adequate physical resources.

The Board of Directors

The highest level of administrative function is the lay board of directors, sometimes referred to as the board of trustees. Since the board represents community auspices and sanction, it should be truly representative. The board of directors should include able and influential leaders representing a broad spectrum of cultural interests, *viz.*, finance, industry, commerce, labor, public office, communication and public relations media, service clubs, and women's organizations. It should also include prominent members in the helping professions of medicine, law, social work and education, as well as selected responsible center members.

All board members should be considered on the basis of their interest and merit, and regardless of race, creed, national origin and/or physical handicap. Responsible and capable blind members from the center should also serve on the board. They will provide an official channel for membership expression regarding the objectives and policies which affect the persons for whom the center exists. The board of directors should be primarily concerned with broad policy-making decisions relating to the continuing validity of the center's purposes and objectives, and with how these are being accomplished through the administration of the center's operations.

The aims and objectives of the specialized center should be clearly formulated in a written statement against which the program of the center may be regularly and frequently evaluated, on the basis of appropriate and valid program data reported by the staff.

The Executive Director and Administrators

All personnel concerned with the outcome of administration should have some part in planning, commensurate with their responsibilities and interests. However, there should be one executive director accountable for carrying out the policies established by and with the board of directors. The executive director should be employed by the board and be directly responsible to the board.

The executive leadership should provide the organizational structure, personnel, management policies, procedures and finances to enable the effective fulfillment of center purposes and objectives. It is essential that the form and content, structure and method of administration be in accordance with the basic philosophy of the center. The quality of administration is a means of implementing center purposes and objectives. The executive director should provide for the efficient coordination of the administrative, supervisory and leadership levels of function, so that there will result the most effective implementation of principles and achievement of center objectives.

The administrative leadership establishes the channels by means of which facilities and equipment may be acquired and maintained; personnel may be employed and developed; appropriate records may be kept; programs may be financed; public relations established, and the entire enterprise evaluated with the staff and the board. No one person performs all these functions. However, to a certain extent, every staff member performs some of them. For example, every staff member is almost continuously a public relations and public education representative of the center. With scrupulous regard for the confidential nature of certain personal information about blind members, a staff worker is a representative of the center, and work for the blind in general, when he discusses his job and the center with neighbors and friends.

Administrative and supervisory management should be structured so that lines of responsibility and authority are understood and accepted by all concerned. It is a sound principle to directly associate responsibility with authority.

Supervisors

In centers in which staff size requires differentiation into the three principal leadership function levels, i.e., administrator, supervisor, and leader, the supervisor should have the primary responsibility for selecting the paid and voluntary workers to carry out the program activities. It should be the responsibility of the supervisor to plan and carry out in-service training programs with instruction-leaders. These programs should be concerned not only with the achievement of program objectives, but also with the needs of the staff members, as those needs relate to center aims and purposes.

Administrative distance places the supervisor in the most advantageous position to determine that facilities, equipment and supplies are maintained in good working condition, and are completely safe for use by the members. In this connection, the supervisor, with supplemental assistance from the activity leaders, should seek constantly for new supplies and equipment, which will enrich the program. This should include the many resources available in scrap materials which may be acquired with little or no expenditure of funds. Volunteers who are employed in appropriate firms, or have relatives or friends in such firms, are good sources for obtaining such scrap materials. Sometimes, even board members enjoy the opportunity to be helpful in this fashion. Many activities in arts and crafts, such as sewing, millinery, knitting and rugmaking can be developed with the use of donated scrap materials.

Employment and Personnel Practices

Employment and personnel practices should insure the selection and retention of properly qualified staff, adequate working conditions, and salary scales commensurate with the qualifications and responsibilities of the various staff positions. Personnel practices, job descriptions, and qualifications should be formulated in writing.

In hiring staff, the professional, training, and experience qualifications of the individual, for the particular position, should be the primary considerations regardless of age, sex, race, creed, national origin or physical disability; unless these latter characteristics will directly interfere with the effective functioning of the individual on the job in question. For example, a totally blind person can not adequately supervise an active swimming program; nor can a certain leader be effective in a group with deep and intensive feelings about religions, races or nationalities.

Notwithstanding the general positiveness of interacting differences, common sense dictates a consideration of the realistic levels of member functioning and understanding. Whenever normal vision is not a fundamental prerequisite, it is desirable to select otherwise qualified visually impaired personnel. Such staff members have served successfully as board members, administrators and supervisors. Blind staff members can be leaders and instructors in music, especially guitar, recorder, and folk song groups, and in discussion and forum groups. Visual handicap should not be a prerequisite for a position.

The stability of a center is a function of a satisfied and developing staff. To promote the recruitment, growth, and retention of staff, administrative and supervisory management should provide policies and practices which strengthen these personnel processes. Altruistic and humanitarian impulses are important ingredients of the motivational factors which direct workers into this field. However, the more tangible rewards for working in a specialized field are nonetheless highly significant in establishing and improving the status and morale of specialized recreation center workers.

Recruitment and retention of adequate staff have been extremely difficult. There seems to have been an erroneous and unfortunate assumption that the negative implications ascribed to blindness apply also to the staff that works with blind persons. The rather obvious fact that work with exceptional individuals requires personnel with exceptional qualifications has been noted more through emotional reference to dedicated individuals than through pragmatic professional considerations. This is why prominent authorities in the field consider that work for the blind is far below the qualitative level of achievement than work with the handicapped in general.

As a noteworthy beginning, salary levels should relate to those prevailing in the area, supplemented by established professional salary standards designed to attract and hold competent personnel. Specialized recreation center studies have shown salaries to be significantly lower than professionally recommended minimums and/or those prevailing in non-specialized recreation centers. Staff morale can also be improved through planful individual and personal supervisory recognition at staff meetings and/or social functions, as well as through fair salary rewards. There should be explicit salary ranges which provide for minimum and maximum pay levels, with reasonable discrete intermediate steps for annual increases on the basis of satisfactory performance.

Staff growth and retention are also aided through purposeful individual and group conferences. Administrative and supervisory staff should consider the conference an essential method of supervision for all center staff members, paid and volunteer. Program and time difficulties must not prevent the development of a system of individual and group conferences which includes full-time and part-time staff members. Because such a large proportion of center employees tend to be part-time workers, scheduled time assignments should provide for such regular conference opportunities. No better supervisory method is known for helping a worker to do a more effective job.

There should be recognition of the fact that non-professional and supportive staff members, such as clerks and maintenance workers, also need considerations which encourage their energies and skills in behalf of center program objectives. In the informal atmosphere of a recreation center, these workers may have frequent and influencing contact with members. Their contribution to the climate of the center will be more positive if they have a basic understanding and appreciation of program purposes and how their assignments and relationships relate to these purposes.

Time of Program

The determination of program duration for the center as a whole, and for individual members in particular, is more often a function of administrative factors than considerations which pertain to the needs of the blind members.

Program Season

Many specialized recreation centers for blind adults operate as subsidiary units of multi-function agencies for the blind. The recreation service is considered an adjunctive or ancillary aspect of the total rehabilitation agency program. Frequently, the parent agency may also include a supplementary camp facility and summer program. As a result, many specialized recreation center programs commence in late September and operate for thirty-five to forty weeks, until early or mid-June.

Key staff workers report for work two to five weeks before the members, to plan and to prepare. They usually stay on for a somewhat shorter period, to close up, evaluate, and record significant information about program and members. Some staff members are used in the agency's supplementary summer program. Operation costs also determine the length of the center season. There is little doubt, however, that the needs of the members dictate a full fifty-two week annual season. Their recreation needs are no less urgent during the summer months, even for those who are able to attend the summer facility for the usual two-week vacation.

Attendance

Administrative factors, i.e., cost of transportation, food, staff, materials, and the size of the facility, generally limit membership attendance to once a week. Center objectives, ability of the member to travel independently, and inclusion of large group activities sometimes permit more frequent attendance for individual members. The presumption of members needs, based on the known characteristics of specialized recreation center members, suggest that two attendances per week is a much more desirable standard, in relation to the objectives of specialized recreation centers for blind adults.

Daily Program Time

Specialized recreation centers for blind adults are usually operated for two to five days a week. Two types of daily sessions are found in operating centers. These are generally characterized as the morning-afternoon session, from about 10:00 o'clock in the morning until about 3:00 o'clock in the afternoon; and the afternoon-evening session, which operates from about 2:00 o'clock in the afternoon until about 9:00 o'clock in the evening. Administrative, membership, and locale factors determine the sessions for particular centers.

The earlier morning-afternoon session is predicated largely on the notion, which is prevalent in senior citizen groups, that leisure time is most pressing during former work time, and that in the evening, the older folks want to be home with their families. The later afternoon-evening sessions preferants claim that most specialized recreation center members need more time for personal preparation in the morning; want the longer recreation program day; enjoy the somewhat more formal, fuller evening meal which is part of program, and actually prefer being away from the family. For many members, the afternoon-evening session seems like a full day away from their confining room or apartment. In the large urban setting, traffic problems make the afternoon-evening session preferable. Of course, daytime programs do encourage independent travel for some members, but this group is very small.

Program Planning

The program of every individual member should be independently planned. Visually impaired persons who need specialized recreation services require skilled selection and grouping of activities. An individual program should provide opportunities for membership participation in both active and passive activities. The encouragement of physical movement should be a dominant objective because immobility is one of the primary resultants of blindness. Considering the strong social isolation factors in blindness, emphasis should be given to group-centered and inter-group activities in which participants can share past and present experiences, in a positive and self-strengthening manner. Nevertheless, there should also be provision for participation in recreation activities in which the member can function alone, as in many arts and crafts activities.

Members should also be able to take part in activities which will give them opportunities for positive experiences in homogeneous as well as heterogeneous groupings based on differentiating factors such as sex, age, race, religion, national origin, intelligence, education, socio-economic status, and other human characteristics

Large mass gatherings of blind individuals should be carefully planned to provide for maximum membership participation in formulating a constructive theme or purpose for the event. Adequate staff should be provided to assist in the preparation and the operation of large mass gatherings, i.e., social dances, in order to promote desirable behavior which is conducive to positive interpersonal contacts, and also in order to avoid the disconcerting confusions and lack of individualizations which tend to over-emphasize and dramatize those effects of blindness which strengthen blindness stereotypes. Without such careful planning and membership involvement, large mass gatherings too easily acquire many of the debilitating characteristics of the historic "bread and circus" for the unfortunates.

In connection with the inclusion of members in all activity program planning, there should be recognition of the fact that many member groups contain potential indigenous leaders who should be provided with opportunities for the utilization and development of their leadership talents.

Finances

Most specialized recreation centers for blind adults are subsidiary units of multi-function agencies for the blind. The specialized recreation center budget is therefore a part of the total agency budget. Although exceptional, there are some centers which operate as individual agencies, e.g., the Phoenix Center for the Blind in Arizona, and the Seattle Social Center for the Blind in Washington.

Numerous factors determine annual per capita costs which range widely from less than one hundred dollars to more than three hundred dollars. Approximation of costs can be computed by considering those cost factors which more directly affect budget, e.g., transportation cost at from two to three dollars per round trip per each member; per meal cost at from one to two dollars; and staff salaries. These are the principal items in budgets of specialized recreation centers that are subsidiary parts of larger organizations which provide the physical facilities, certain basic equipment, and maintenance service associated with site and buildings.

The administrative leadership of the agency and/or the center should provide the personnel, policies, and procedures which will provide the finances to enable the effective operation of the center. Administration should planfully develop a broad base for continued and substantial fund raising from private and public sources. Accredited methods of fund solicitation should be utilized. Fund raising should not control or unfavorably influence program functioning or the attainment of program objectives. This is sometimes easier said than done. Too often, the motives which engender donations are more deeply affected by presenting blind individuals in pitiful and helpless roles. Usually, desperate fund raising efforts are self-defeating in relation to the purposes and objectives of the center. For example, the utilization of blind members as direct solicitors of funds and materials denigrates the center, work for the blind, and most of all the members themselves. There can be no justification for a program that destroys its own foundation. The shoring up of the trembling edifice soon becomes the dominant objective of administration, and the members tend to be used as pawns in the service of the institution.

There is no substantive dichotomy between program aims and ethical fund raising when both are housed in the same philosophical framework of principles, where both belong. When the need for the center is well established, when the auspices for the center are soundly representative, and when the administration is effective, resourceful and imaginative; public education and public relations will result in adequate support for the program. Relatively large sums for capital and operating expenses should be solicited through methods and practices which are in general concordance with the code of fund raising principles developed by the American Association of Workers for the Blind.

There are internal policies and practices which have an effect on center financing. Every effort is required to guarantee the most effective use of donated funds. Waste of equipment, materials and costly services such as light, heat and telephone must be kept to a minimum. Members who can afford to meet all or part of the cost of materials and services should be expected to do so. All staff and members should be aware of their potentialities as community informants about the center program. The special interests of individual donors and/or foundations should be planfully exploited for center program support. Special areas in which public funds may be available for regularly recurrent services, such as transportation, should be explored with the appropriate public organizations. Finally, a properly audited financial report should be made public annually, in conjunction with valid and meaningful statistics presented simply, yet dramatically.

Records and Reports

Records serve many essential purposes which directly affect program. Analogy to administration is apropos. Administration is a means to program achievement. Records are devices which serve to portray, compare and evaluate program activity and achievement.

Administratively, records serve the purpose of fiscal and prudential accountability to the board of directors and to the community of donors whom they represent. Every center should establish effective methods for recording and reporting significant and valid business and financial information including copies of budget, payroll and other expenditures. Administration is also concerned with basic program data concerning the number of enrolled members, monthly intake, and attendance frequencies. Other record and report forms include personnel applications, accident report forms, petty cash requisitions, and purchase forms. Special reports are often prepared to appeal for funds, equipment, and materials, and/or to inform and influence current and future program planning.

These latter data are sometimes included in a descriptive annual statement, which accompanies the annual statistical report.

On the supervisory level, the preceding administrative reports need to be supplemented with additional content relative to individual activity attendances. It should also contain personal information about the members, as individuals, and their behavior in program activities. It is at this point that a sharp distinction can be discerned in the quality and quantity of recording. The difference is classic and fundamental, and represents one of the distinguishing characteristics between professional recreation and social group work. In organized recreation, recording of membership behavior is minimal, even where individual member report forms exist. Usually, only extreme behavior is noted, in addition to a listing of activities and expenditures for the season. In social group work, the written account of a member's continual behavior in the group serves as the principal method and tool for evaluating the member's progress and the worker's achievement. The carefully documented case record is indispensable to social group work supervision. In this connection, it is important to point out that objective and pertinent case recording requires trained skill and is time consuming. Supervisory case record study also requires trained skill and is time consuming. The resulting supervisory conference, for behavior evaluation, diagnosis and prognosis, is time consuming, and the supportive clerical processes involved in the physical making of the case record, typing, filing, and storage are expensive. However, it should be emphasized that all records should serve the best interest of the member for whom the center exists. Records should be regularly scrutinized to make sure they serve important center purposes.

The basic records used in most specialized recreation centers include the following: (1) an intake card or form with essential personal and demographic data, health facts with recommendations from the member's physician, as well as explicit information about whom to notify in case of emergency; (2) an individual program activity card which is filled out seasonally, in conference with a staff member; (3) a volunteer registration and activity assignment card on which seasonal notations are made regarding attendance, punctuality and effectiveness. Numerous other forms may be utilized, dependent upon center program objectives and the availability of resources for the preparation, completion, and use of the records and reports. Again, the basic criterion must be better service for the member. Certain of these forms have been standardized by professional and service organizations.[1] Many university texts include suggested forms.[2] Centers usually adapt these recommended forms to meet their specific conditions and needs.

Site and Facilities

Specialized recreation centers for blind adults are usually located on sites and in buildings which house the parent multi-function welfare and rehabilitation organization. Nevertheless, the basic principles which apply to the location and structure of the larger unit apply as well to the subsidiary recreation center.

In choosing a site, careful attention should be given to the current and future stability of the neighborhood, i.e., its general character, legal zoning, the availability of public utilities and adequate public transportation. Because restricted mobility and dependent travel are intrinsic effects of blindness, the center should be located in relation to the prevalent residential densities of the blind members to be served. Accessibility is also important for staff, and for those members who can travel independently under reasonable circumstances. Accessibility to public view and visit are significant influencing factors in public relations and fund raising.

Though most centers are located in urban areas where desirable land is at a premium, the site should be sufficiently large to accommodate the building, with ample car parking area. There should be some provision for appropriate and seasonal outdoor recreation activities, picnic grill, and a walking area which can be used for dancing, and games such as deck shuffleboard. If possible, there should be some landscaping. The atmosphere and character of the site and the physical plant should create an impression of friendliness and warmth through form, design, and color. The National Rec-

[1]Morton Thompson: *Starting a Recreation Program in Institutions for the Ill or Handicapped Aged.* New York, National Recreation Association, 1960, pp. 11-12, 16.

[2]The Athletic Institute: *The Recreation Program.* Chicago, 1954, pp. 135-145; 160-162.

reation Association has developed specific recommendations and standards for various types of recreation facilities.[3]

Adaptations

The design of the building should allow for future expansion without major material alterations. Every effort should be made to wed function and utility with building necessities and economic expediencies. Multiple use of facilities and equipment should be carefully considered, to assure the most varied and effective recreation service. Except for highly specialized activity facilities for bowling and swimming, most other purely physical units can be used for multiple purposes. A physical exercise room can be used for reading and discussion groups, if the room is well ventilated and chairs are stored nearby; dining rooms can be used for club meetings; if appropriate closets are available, the dining room can easily become a game room; and by moving some tables and chairs, dancing can be taught to small groups.

In addition to providing space and appropriate equipment for a wide variety of recreation activities and experiences, a center should include necessary private offices for staff, a conference room of suitable size, a waiting room for visitors, ample storage space, rest room facilities for staff and participants, a first aid room, coat room, public toilets, public telephones, and reception and/or entrance and exit arrangements which will safeguard the security of the building. With more than two stories, elevators are a necessity for most of the members. Experience indicates that for older blind persons, an elevator operator is preferable to the self-service automated elevator. Member traffic on and off the elevator needs to be directed by a staff member.

Extensive adaptation of facilities or equipment is not necessary because of blindness and/or the relatively older years of the specialized recreation center population. Some considerations are helpful because these not only contribute to safety, but also facilitate and encourage independent movement, a primary objective of the program. For example, it is helpful if the several floor plans have a generally similar design, i.e., hallways, exits, toilets, offices, and

[3]The National Recreation Association: *Planning a Community Recreation Building*. New York, 1955, p. 220.

activity areas. Long main hallways should be straight, unencumbered, and not too wide. A convenient hip-high (about thirty-six inches high) guide rail encourages swifter and more confident movement—avoids groping and shuffling. Sharp corners at sudden turns should be bull-nosed. Sound cues are helpful for locating important and/or dangerous entrances and exits. For example, a continuous fifteen-second interval sound chime is a pleasant and welcomed clue to the main entrance for members who travel independently. Doors which open on to dangerous landings should make a distinctive warning sound upon opening, or the inside doorknob should have a distinctive shape or knurled surface. Men's and women's rest rooms and toilets can be identified in similar fashion. Health permitting, walking the stairs should be advocated. Such movement and exercise is encouraged, when convenient hand rails are provided on both sides of the stairway. In consideration of the older members, the stairs should not have abrupt (square) nosing, and floors should have nonslip surfaces.[4]

Swinging doors, such as fire doors, can be dangerous for blind persons. Wherever possible these and other frequently used doors should be of the sliding variety. More than one half of specialized recreation center participants have some usable vision. Optimum lighting with planful use of wall, ceiling and floor colors, affect general tone and atmosphere as well as promote indoor mobility and safety.

Observation of program activities by interested staff, donors, and community representatives is a necessary reality if handled discreetly and wisely. The dignity and self-respect of members are fundamental considerations. The abundant use of glass partition is desirable, for this makes necessary observation unobtrusive and least disturbing to program. Such provisions are especially recommended for the swimming pool in order to keep spectators off the floors used by the swimmers. Observation from outside the room of an activity permits explanations which are not appropriate in the actual presence of members.

The New York Association for the Blind, the largest volun-

[4]American Standards Company: *American Standards Specifications for Making Buildings and Facilities Accessible to, and Usable by, the Physically Handicapped.* New York, 1961, p. 9.

tary agency for the blind in the world, includes facilities for many recreation activities, *viz.*, swimming pool with appropriate locker, toilet, storage, and observation provisions; two regulation automatic bowling alleys with lockers and an area for spectators; a small gym and exercise room; a large auditorium with modern stage, lighting board and two dressing rooms; necessary public telephones, toilets, cloak rooms, visitors' lobby, and a good size meeting room with an adjoining pantry-kitchen for smaller parties, club-meetings and functions.

On the main recreation floor are located a large dining room, with a capacity for one hundred twenty-five diners, and, of course, a modern kitchen. The ceramics room, with ample storage space and outlets for the necessary voltage for several kilns, has eight tables with two chairs per table. A fully supplied arts and crafts unit can accommodate sixteen members comfortably. Four sewing rooms, a music room, typing room, game room, and lounge with sink, stove and refrigerator complete the principal facilities on this floor. There are three staff offices, toilets, and several large storage closets.

In addition, several large rooms in other parts of the new building have been designed for use by drama groups, forums, clubs, dance classes, staff conferences, and any other special recreation functions. Most of the enumerated facilities, except those particularly specialized, such as the swimming pool, the bowling alleys, the ceramics and the crafts units, can be used for multiple purposes. For example, the music room will also be used for reading groups, discussion groups, club meetings and even small parties, because it is so near the lounge kitchen unit. Of course, the auditorium is used for large functions, such as dramatic presentations, dances, roller-skating, professional conferences, and major fund-raising events.

The National Recreation Association has recommended certain minimum facilities for the effective operation of a small community recreation center: (1) an auditorium or assembly hall with removable seats or a gymnasium; (2) lounge for informal reading and quiet games or discussions; (3) room for a specialized activity like arts and crafts, workshop or game room, and (4) two rooms for clubs, hobby groups, or other multiple use.[5]

Public Relations

The specialized recreation center for blind adults begins as an expression of community interest and concern for the needs and well-being of fellow citizens who are blind. Though the need for the specialized recreation service is valid, only a relatively few members of the community may perceive the need, and sanction its gratification through the creation of a center. Thus it becomes a continuous responsibility for the center to extend information about its program, to enlarge community interest in the program, and to marshal and engage greater community resources for the program.

The board of directors and the top executives and administrative leaders are charged with the primary responsibility for public education and fund raising. Most emphatically, however, every staff member, paid and volunteer, is an important element in the continuing process of informing the public and enlisting public interest. To a lesser extent but, at times, more effectively, the handicapped members themselves serve as ambassadors of the center.

Adequate publicity must be supported by adequate program achievements. However, publicity practices should zealously safeguard the interest and the right of self-determination of the members. Many members are delighted to cooperate in efforts to inform the public about the program as well as to show off their particular notable achievements.

Safety

A frequently used persuasion, in the vocational placement of blind individuals, is the alleged fact that blind persons are less prone to industrial accidents than sighted persons. Nonetheless, in the more complicated and varied activity environment of the specialized recreation center, considerable foreseeability of accident potential is strongly advised. Staff and participants should have the necessary knowledge, skills, and attitudes about personal and group safety in the use of equipment and materials, and in general mobility. A

[5]National Recreation Association: *Schedule for the Appraisal of Community Recreation.* New York, 4th printing, 1957, pp. 13-14.

common sense awareness of hazards precludes much grief, pain, strain, filling out forms, and expense.

Safety consciousness quickly engenders the mundane habit of pushing unused chairs as close to tables as possible; fully opening or closing hinged doors; moving furniture, equipment, and other obstacles back to their accustomed locations, or making proper announcement of necessary changes. Totally blind persons have been hurt because they have tried to sit down on a chair which someone has unthinkingly and quietly moved. A dropped sixteen-pound bowling ball may cause serious foot injury. Bowlers should be urged to get their fingers in the holes of the ball before lifting it off the rack. Some visually handicapped members have to be taught how to bend to retrieve a dropped article. Too often, members will hit the sharp edge of a table because they bend over, rather than bend down with the knees.

Safety is an interesting subject for discussion which requires little motivation. Members are eager to find out, and to be helpful. There should be regular and frequent review of necessary and protective safety aspects of the center program. A safety committee, with staff and member representatives supplemented by insurance and safety advisers, adds another informative and useful activity to program.

Safety concerns should begin with the member's admittance to the center. Those programs which operate as separate entities (not affiliated with multi-function agencies in which cleared and selected clients are referred for center membership) should, as an important aspect of their intake process, require physical and other reports so that programming and supervision will consider activity limitations and safeguards for particular members. Trained and competent first-aid personnel should be available during program activities. In view of the handicap, and the general debility characteristics of the older members, it is desirable and reassuring to have a nurse around. She may perhaps be useful also as an activity leader, e.g., conduct groups in home nursing, first aid, or just general personal and public health.

Administrative and supervisory personnel should be familiar with the explicit procedures operative in emergency situations of member illness and accident. They should know when and how to call an ambulance, doctor, priest, relatives, and to notify the executive leadership when serious complications arise. Emergency telephone numbers should be prominently posted. If the center has a switchboard, the operator should have these numbers instantly available upon notification from the responsible administrator or supervisor.

Experience indicates that panic is more potent, and more frightful, when the individuals involved are blind. The utmost consideration should be given to fire-proofed and fire-protected facilities, equipment, and materials. The interest and suggestions of local fire department officials should be sought. Incidentally, they also can serve as informative lecturers and discussion leaders. Their recommendations for fire-drill procedures should be rigorously followed—and of course, all such emergencies should be drills, even when there is smoke. Arrangements for assisting totally blind members should be carefully detailed and circulated. It is not wise to be careless about any safety precautions. Liability as well as humanity are direct functions of foreseeability, concern and responsibility.

Maintenance and Housekeeping

The characteristic location of most specialized recreation centers in buildings which house the parent organization, underscores the interpretation of specialized recreation for blind adults as an integral component of rehabilitation. The proximate location of the center within the physical context of the multiple service agency makes the regular agency maintenance and housekeeping services available to the center. In such situations, the center administration has but nimimum responsibility for these necessary components of facilities management. It is clear, however, that even in these fortuitous situations, the recreation service needs to concern itself with maintenance and housekeeping. Program size and content determine the extent of assistance needed. On a general basis, programs with approximately one hundred members per session need a full-time maintenance man and a full-time housekeeping worker. Activity programs which make multiple use of available facilities need assistance in moving tables, chairs, pianos and other equipment. Parties and entertainment leave facilities in a mess.

Recreation staff workers should not be expected to do maintenance and housekeeping chores, although they often must, in order to conduct activities. A dance teacher usually will not wait for the maintenance man to come to clear the room of chairs and tables. With the help of some of the members, the task is completed, often just as the maintenance man arrives. Staff can assist in this difficult area by careful management of equipment and supplies. Each worker has the responsibility of putting away the materials which belong in closets and cupboards. Activity areas should be left in reasonable order. This means that many leaders must take and/or assign responsibility for basic cleanup after an activity.

The general cleaning of the building and its individual facilities takes place after activity program hours. In large centers, specially oriented maintenance men are assigned to specific tasks such as keeping the swimming pool in legal and safe condition, and giving the bowling alleys the special care needed to keep them in satisfactory condition for the competitive bowlers.

Adequate maintenance and housekeeping are essential to safety, economy, staff and member morale, public interest and support, and the achievement of the aims and purposes of the center.

Evaluation

As a process, evaluation is an essential element of a dynamic and developing human organism and/or human institution. Neither program activity, nor program expansion, can be accepted as evidence of program achievement, since neither activity nor expansion should be, in themselves, objectives of program. The mere process of wanting to know, of inquiring and exploring, and of judging the validity and meaning of reported as well as demonstrated accomplishments, serves to keep a program viable and growing. The continual utilization of basic principles to guide evaluation, judgment and planning make this process an essential of program operation.

Evaluation is a professional obligation. The trained worker understands the common human tendency to become so immersed in process and activity, that sense of direction is lost. Before long, the goals and objectives of the center are obscured. Workers become busier and busier but proceed backwards because they are heading in the wrong direction. The essence of the supervisory process is interpretation and evaluation, followed by understanding and growth.

Evaluation should not consist solely of an effort to justify, or of a search for program elements which can be used for exploitive purposes. It is not unethical to be aware of member and center accomplishments and to properly present these as demonstrable evidence of achievement and worth. However, there should be no shrinking from the discovery of weaknesses. Evaluation must be as objective as possible and conducted genuinely. Valid conclusions cannot be derived from biased data. The professional worker is distinguished by his secure attitude toward honest questioning of his performance.

Program evaluation is treated comprehensively in many scholarly recreation and social group work textbooks. Professionally directed recreation programs usually include suggested staff appraisal schedules. The very process of developing such an instrument denotes an intelligent and wholesome appreciation of research and evaluation. In 1955, the Recreation Commission, City of Long Beach, California, developed a "*How 'm I Doing*" Chart which is discussed on page 141 and will be of great value in program and personnel evaluation.

Chapter VIII

OPERATIONAL PRINCIPLES

Introduction

IN THE literal translation from the Latin *principeum*, principle means "beginning," not in the sense of time, but in the sense of reason. Yet principles are concepts which result from inductive and deductive experiences affecting the human condition. Human experiences have emotional content. Thus principles are expressions of both logic and values. Civilizations began, developed and ebbed in relation to existent or non-existent principles. These principles served to guide the evolutionary courses of man as he sought to survive and enhance both his individuality and sociality. Operational principles are primary guides for the formulation, implementation and evaluation of policies, procedures and practices in social institutions.

Studies of specialized recreation centers have revealed serious discrepancies between expressed objectives, and practices for their attainment. Many such centers tend to function as microcosms in a sea of community organizations. The lack of "inter" and intra-institutional communication is due, in large measure, to the absence of specified principles which most workers can accept with honest conviction. In the descriptive-status study of major specialized recreation centers for blind adults in New York City in 1963, ninety-nine operational principles were formulated and validated.[1] Central and prominent principles were developed in eight major areas of institutional functioning: (a) philosophy (interpretations); (b) objectives; (c) auspices; (d) people served; (e) activity pro-

[1]Maurice Case: A Manual for the Operation of Recreation Programs in Specialized Recreation Centers for Blind Adults. Unpublished Doctor's dissertation, New York University, 1963, pp. 334-84.

gram; (f) leadership; (g) administration, and (h) profession. These validated principles are a concise summarization of the preceding chapters and may serve to emphasize the desirability of frequent evaluation and appraisal to safeguard the resources and integrity of the individuals served, the staff and the community.

(a) *Philosophy and Interpretations*

1. The furtherance of individual self-realization through opportunities for activities and experience which liberate and satisfy the intrinsic needs of every citizen should be the central purpose of democracy.
2. For many blind adults, visual impairment should be considered a severely disabling handicap, which significantly limits opportunities to liberate and satisfy intrinsic needs, and opportunities for self-realization.
3. The specialized recreation center should be considered a socially valid institution because its essential function is to provide opportunities for activities and experiences which liberate and satisfy intrinsic needs of blind adults, thus serving also as a preventive and therapeutic instrumentality for the mental and physical health of individuals and the community.

(b) *Objectives*

4. The specialized recreation center should provide its participants with opportunities for the greatest variety of individual, group, and inter-group experiences, qualitatively and quantitatively, which meet recreation needs and wants so that maximum individual satisfaction will result with individual and group values enhanced through maximum interaction with the animate and inanimate environment.
5. The specialized recreation center should be a community facility in which a blind individual may experience a self-strengthening consciousness of kind through positive identification and sharing with similarly handicapped individuals, the problems and stresses concomitant with visual impairment in a sight-oriented society.
6. The specialized rcreation center should continually emphasize the restoration factor implicit in rehabilitation by providing the greatest variety of rcreation experiences, qualitatively and quantitatively, in a climate which promotes

self-regard, self-determination and independence, so that the handicapped individual can increasingly participate in ever-widening areas of specialized and non-specialized recreation activities.

(c) *Auspices*

7. Every community and/or group of contiguous communities should have a special committee charged with thinking and planning to provide through public and/or private auspices, opportunities for the constructive use of leisure time of isolated and inactive blind individuals who reside in this area.
8. The existence of the specialized recreation center should be based upon the determined recreation needs of blind individuals who require specialized recreation service as revealed through sound, cooperative and continued community inquiry and research.
9. The specialized recreation center should complement and supplement, and not compete with, other regular or specialized recreation centers; and should establish definite patterns of cooperative relationships with the other centers as well as with the existing coordinating community council.
10. The legal authorization (charter), and/or constitution, and/or organizational directives should be sufficiently broad in scope to allow for changes in function to accommodate changes in community and participant needs, and to permit experimentation with new programs which may provide more effective service in relation to the objectives of the center.

(d) *People*

11. There should be recognition that for some blind adults the specialized recreation center program might be needed only temporarily, while for others the program might represent an optimal level of rehabilitation and in many instances, habilitation.
12. The specialized recreation center should not be composed entirely of visually handicapped persons because such complete segregation would tend to overstress common individual and social hardships resulting from blindness and limit opportunities for positive and varying recreation experiences which link individuals with reality and society.

13. The specialized recreation center should planfully include selected, trained and supervised sighted volunteer workers in order to promote maximization of recreation experiences for the members, as well as to provide educational and social experiences for the sighted individuals who upon their return to the community will act as emissaries of the center.

(e) *Activity Program*

General Considerations

14. The specialized recreation center program should be conducted in a manner and by methods consistent with the interpretations and objectives of the center; and any activity introduced into the program should be considered in terms of its potential for contributing to the purposes and objectives of the center.
15. There should be due recognition of social science findings which indicate that more desirable development and achievement result when group and/or individual relationships occur within a democratic as opposed to an autocratic milieu.
16. In planning program, use should be made of standards developed by national recreation associations and societies with such modifications as may be expedient to meet the particular needs of particular groups in a particular community; but such modifications should be minimal and necessary for reasonable and constructive participation and achievement.
17. The program of every member should be carefully and individually planned because blind individuals who need specialized recreation services require skilled grouping and activity selection.
18. The specialized recreation center program should provide opportunities for membership participation in both active and passive activities, and encourage physical movement because immobility is one of the primary resultants of visual deprivation. An individual is more a part of his environment when he moves in it.
19. The center should provide opportunities for individuals to have recreation experiences alone, but considering the strong social isolation factors in blindness, emphasis should be given to the group-centered and inter-group activities in which participants can share past and present experiences in a positive and self-strengthening fashion.

20. Large mass gatherings of blind participants should be carefully planned to provide for maximum membership participation in formulating a constructive theme or purpose, and in preparation and operation of the activity with the assistance of adequate staff, paid and/or volunteer, in order to promote acceptable behavior conducive to positive interpersonal contacts, and in order to avoid the confusions and lack of individualizations which tend to over-emphasize and dramatize effects of blindness.
21. The specialized recreation center program should provide for a maximum of membership opportunities for positive experiences in homogeneous as well as heterogeneous groupings based on differentiating factors like sex, age, race, national origin, intelligence, religion, education, socio-economic status, intellectual and/or physical capacities and other human characteristics.
22. There should be recognition of the fact that many groups contain potential indigenous leaders who should be provided with maximum opportunities for developing and utilizing their leadership talents.
23. Centers should select activities and experiences which have strong carry-over and extension values in relation to home use by individuals; for even in their own homes, opportunities for meeting recreation needs may be limited.
24. Centers should provide for activities through which the blind participants can make, through their strengths and skills, some contribution to other members or groups in the community.
25. There should be significant recognition of the importance of social climate in the center, as this is influenced by staff and participant attitudes, so that there will be a lessening of the stigma of blindness and a strengthening of individual appraisal and self-regard.
26. There should be sufficient recognition of even simple achievements which are earned by special toil because of blindness, but there should not be insincere or suffusive praise for mediocrity, nor excessive debilitating solicitude.
27. Because many of the blind members frequently have unmet non-recreation needs, the specialized recreation centers which are not affiliated with comprehensive rehabilitation agencies should provide competent consultation and referral

services, and be located where the needed ancillary services are readily available; and have a close cooperative liaison with such community resources.

ECONOMIC CONSIDERATIONS

28. Because blindness and restricted mobility inevitably necessitate costly transportation, the specialized recreation center should explore the availability of public welfare or public recreation funds for regularly recurrent program expense items.
29. The specialized recreation center should plan its program in relation to the economic capacities of the blind individuals to be served; no financially needy blind person should be denied service; and selective fee charging for membership, special activities, meals and materials should be utilized only to enhance the blind person's status and self-regard; and to promote greater participant involvement in program operations.

GEOGRAPHIC CONSIDERATIONS

30. The specialized recreation center should plan its program in relation to the physical and cultural resources of the community and make full use of such resources.
31. Because lessened outdoor mobility is a perdominant factor in blindness, the specialized recreation center should plan its facilities and program in relation to the locational density of the blind individuals to be served, and should take into consideration modes of travel and transportation, including their costs.

FACILITIES CONSIDERATIONS

32. Special construction features which will contribute to safety, as well as encourage independent mobility, should be included, i.e., reasonably straight halls free of unnecessary obstructions, easily identifiable doors to toilets and exits to stairwells; and for those participants with some usable vision optimum lighting and coloring.
33. Centers should provide personnel and participants with knowledge, skills and attitudes relating to personal and group safety in the use of equipment and materials; i.e., routine habits of putting chairs close to tables, fully opening or clos-

ing hinged doors, participation in monthly fire and emergency drills, and in being aware of and reporting discovered program hazards.

34. In choosing a site, attention should be paid to general current and future stability of the neighborhood, the availability of public utilities, transportation, pleasant surroundings, avoidance of neighborhood nuisances, and general accessibility.
35. The site should be sufficiently large to accommodate the building with ample parking and car storage area, as well as landscaping and outdoor activity areas, and the design should provide for future expansion without major material alterations.
36. The atmosphere and character of the physical plant should create an impression of friendliness and warmth; it should not be severe, imposing or forbidding, i.e., institutional.
37. Multiple use of facilities and equipment should be considered in planning and operation to assure most effective and efficient recreation service.
38. In addition to providing space and appropriate equipment for the greatest variety of recreation activities and experiences, including food preparation and dining, there should be necessary private offices for staff, a conference room of suitable size, a waiting room for visitors, ample storage space, conveniently located rest room facilities for staff and participants, public toilets, public telephones, a first-aid room, and a receptionist location which will adequately safeguard the building.

TIME CONSIDERATIONS

39. Specialized recreation centers should operate throughout the year because the economic and social resources of the participants are generally limited.
40. Frequency of attendance and daily program time should be determined by the needs of the participants in relation to the resources of the agency and its purposes and objectives.

ACTIVITY SELECTION CONSIDERATIONS

41. The center program should be sufficiently broad in scope and depth of activities and experiences to meet the varieties of recreation needs based on individual and cultural factors like age, sex, capacity, ability, experience and interest.

42. The specialized recreation center program should include activities and experiences which will tend to utilize and strengthen the remaining perceiving senses of the members in order to promote reality links and the reorganization of the individual to optimum functioning despite sight impairment.
43. The specialized recreation center should provide opportunity for the participant to make something of beauty in line, form, color, sound, or graceful use of his own body, and/or in appreciation of what others do if he cannot himself use these forms of expression.
44. The program should provide opportunities for participants to know, learn and use a few songs so they can sing when they feel like it; and to experience rhythm in some way.
45. Specialized recreation center programs which include partaking of food and refreshments should provide facilities and food service which will promote pleasant, unhurried comradeship; while also giving attention to the social aspects of eating related to table skills and dining deportment.

Evaluation Considerations

46. The specialized recreation center should establish effective methods for recording and reporting program activities and member statuses so that regular, frequent, and valid evaluations can be made; evaluations based on demonstrated operations and accomplishments.
47. The specialized recreation center program should provide for planful and purposeful recognition of individual and group achievements in order that participants may experience a strengthening sense of accomplishment.

Protective Considerations

48. The specialized recreation center which is unaffiliated with a comprehensive rehabilitation or welfare organization should, as a part of its intake process, require physical and other reports for all regularly attending members so that programming and supervision may include consideration of activity and other program limitations.
49. Trained and competent first-aid personnel should be available during program activities.
50. Administrative and supervising personnel should be familiar

with the procedures operative in emergency situations of member illness and accident, i.e., when and how to call an ambulance, doctor, priest and relatives.

51. The specialized center program should include a formal organized procedure for orienting new members to the facility, staff, and membership program.
52. Individual orientation and independent movement should be continually promoted through the appropriate use of brailled materials, guide rails, special door knobs, and continued instructional tours guided by staff and/or selected members.

(f) *Leadership*

General Considerations

53. The center should have sufficient personnel in the various staff classifications, i.e., advisory, administrative, supervisory, instructional and/or leader, for the effective achievement of the program's purposes and objectives.
54. Staff should possess adequate physical, mental, emotional, and social abilities as well as necessary recreation and/or group work skills required for successful performance on the three staff functional levels.
55. Center personnel should possess the basic professional and legal qualifications of their respective professions or disciplines.
56. In addition to the professional and legal qualifications, leaders should possess the following:
    a. The physical health to perform the assigned job.
    b. An adequate sense of humor and balance.
    c. An outgoing enthusiasm which reaches out to people.
    d. Sufficient knowledge of the history and developments in the specialized field of "work for the blind."
57. Recognition should be given to the exceptional strain on staff which is concomitant with giving direct service to members in specialized recreation centers, so that time schedules will permit the most adequate performance possible without harm to the leader's physical, mental, emotional or social well-being.
58. Leaders should know, understand, and have a complete sympathy with the purposes and aims of the center, but this does not imply complete agreement with any one method that might be used to achieve particular objectives.

59. The leaders should have a broad understanding of the field of social group work and of recreation.

VOLUNTEER CONSIDERATIONS

60. The volunteer should be recognized as an important program resource, as an advisory member, fund-raiser, instructional-leader or assistant, integration link, community link within and without, general program assistant for innumerable routine tasks like serving refreshments, guiding and transportation.
61. Leaders should be aware of the significant contributions possible by well-oriented and well-supervised volunteers in relation to the promotion of the proper climate and attitudes which will tend to weaken blindness stereotypes within and outside the center.
62. Procedures and practices for the selection, orientation, supervision, and evaluation of volunteers should be explicitly formulated and implemented.
63. Volunteers whose attitudes and behavior persistently tend to strengthem the blindness stereotypes should be referred for appropriate supervisory and/or administrative consultation with the object of either re-assignment to activities requiring little or no contact with members, or if this is not possible, suggesting a transfer of interest to another community agency.

(g) *Administration*

64. The Board of Directors should include able and influential leaders representing a broad spectrum of cultural interests, viz.: finance, industry, commerce, labor, public office, communication and public relations media, service clubs, women's organizations, prominent members in the helping professions of medicine, law, social work, and education; executives from other service agencies for the blind; selected, responsible blind participants; and if not already included in the preceding, members of the "society" of the community.
65. The Board of Directors should include able membership-participant representation to serve as an official channel for membership expression.
66. The Board of Directors should be concerned primarily with the broad policy-making decisions in matters relating to the

continuing validity of the center's purposes and objectives, and how these are being accomplished through the administration of the center's operations.

67. The administrative leadership should coordinate the functions of organization, management, supervision, and instructional leadership, so that all operations are directed toward the most effective achievement of the purposes and objectives of the center as developed with the Board of Trustees.
68. The administrative leadership should provide the organizational structure, personnel, policies, procedures and finances to enable the effective fulfillment of program purposes and objectives.
69. The form and content (structure and method) of administration should be in accordance with the basic philosophy of the center and should be considered a means of implementing its interpretations and achieving its objectives.
70. The aims and objectives of the specialized recreation center should be clearly formulated in a written statement against which the program of the center may be regularly and frequently evaluated on the basis of appropriate and valid program data reported by the staff.
71. Although all persons concerned with the outcome of administration should have some part in planning commensurate with their responsibilities and interests, there should be one executive director accountable for carrying out the policies established by and with the Board of Directors.
72. Administrative leadership in management should establish the channels by means of which facilities and equipment may be maintained, personnel may be employed and developed, records may be kept, programs may be financed, and public relations established, to carry out the aims and objectives of the organization.
73. There should be employment and personnel practices which insure the selection of properly qualified staff, adequate working conditions and a salary scale commensurate with staff training and job responsibilities. Personnel practices, job descriptions and qualifications should be formulated in writing.
74. The administrative and supervisory management of the center should be structured so that direct lines of responsibility

and authority are established which are understood and accepted by all concerned.

75. In specialized recreation centers where staff size necesssitates three staff levels of function, i.e., administratir, supervisor, and leader, the supervisor should have the principal responsibility for selecting paid and unpaid staff to effectively carry on the program.
76. The professional training and experience qualifications of the individual for the job should be the primary considerations regardless of age, sex, race, creed, national origin or physical disability, unless these latter factors would directly interfere with effective functioning on the particular job.
77. Recognition should be given to the need of the members of the specialized recreation center to have contact with a staff composed of both men and women.
78. Recognition should be given to the need of members of the specialized recreation center to have contact with a staff composed of both blind and seeing persons.
79. Planned regular staff conferences, individual and group, should be considered an essential supervisory method of in-service training and staff evaluation which will serve to foster staff growth, cooperation, high morale, and more effective achievement of center objectives.
80. In the utilization of part-time staff, every effort should be made to schedule assignments and working time so that such workers will be available for participation in individual and group conferences.
81. The supervisor should be responsible for ascertaining that all facilities, equipment and supplies are maintained in good working condition, and are completely safe for use by participants.
82. The supervisor and the instructional leader should seek constantly for new supplies and equipment that will enhance the program. This should include the rich resources that are available in scrap materials and which may be secured with little or no expenditure of funds.
83. Salary levels should relate to those prevailing in the area, supplemented by the established professional salary standards designed to attract and hold competent personnel.
84. Promotion of general staff morale should be achieved through individual and personal supervisory recognition of

work quality and through fair salary rewards, as well as through dignified overt group recognition at staff meetings and/or social functions.

85. There should be specified salary ranges providing for minimum and maximum pay with discrete intermediate steps for automatic time increases on the basis of satisfactory performance.
86. All the principles with respect to professional staff should be observed in the selection, training and supervision of the clerical and maintenance personnel.
87. The agency should meet generally accepted standards of responsible operation in areas such as business procedures, insurance coverage, provision for health and safety of members and staff, and record-keeping.
88. Centers should provide for a regular annual, or more frequent, review of necessary protective aspects of the program by a safety committee representative of staff and members, and including insurance and safety advisors.

PUBLIC RELATIONS CONSIDERATIONS

89. The specialized recreation center should devise methods of publicity, public education, and solicitation of funds which will safeguard the interests of both the contributors and the members served, as well as promote achievement of the objectives of the center.
90. Center personnel and membership should be made aware of their continuous role as community informants about the center's objectives and accomplishments.
91. Administration should planfully develop a broad base for continued and substantial fund raising from private and public sources utilizing accredited methods of solicitation.
92. Fund raising should not control or unfavorably influence program functioning or the attainment of program objectives.
93. In raising funds for capital and operating expenses, the code of good practices established by the American Association of Workers for the Blind should be followed.
94. A properly audited financial report should be made public annually.

(h) *Professions*

95. Active membership in professional and service local and

national recreation and group work organizations should be encouraged; and attendance at professional institutes and conferences should be facilitated.

96. The center should provide the means by which leaders may secure additional training through in-service programs as a part of agency work; through granting permission to leaders to attend training sessions by colleges, groups of agencies or other training centers. This should be included as part of the leader's time on the job.
97. Agencies should establish methods for promotion in salary levels. These methods should take into consideration the fact that one who achieves in a direct leadership level is of great value to the agency, and should be able to attain higher salary levels without assuming supervisory responsibilities. There is a need for and there should be a salary for the "master leader."
98. The center should maintain a staff library stocked with standard and current professional writings, and promote frequent use of the materials through regular discussional meetings.
99. The specialized recreation center leadership should be continuously alert to developments in the social service professions which may result in changes in methods and materials which will enhance participant achievement and/or center accomplishments.

Finally, evidence continues to accumulate that perhaps it is better to pause, do nothing, rather than go backwards in the name of beneficence.

Chapter IX

SPECIALIZED PROGRAM FACTORS

Intake

IN THE multi-service agency for blind individuals, where recreation is included as an adjunctive function, clients who are adjudged in need of recreation are referred to the recreation unit. Sometimes the agency intake or social service workers recommend general or specific activities for particular clients. Communication between the functional units is via intra-agency forms supplemented by worker contacts. The referral forms contain basic personal and social data. Usually, the agency case record is available for study by the recreation supervisor. A visually handicapped individual applying directly to the recreation unit, personally or through a source outside the agency, is referred for interview and determination of need for recreation to the regular intake section of the agency.

Some specialized recreation centers are distinct organizational units operating somewhat as a settlement house or a "Y." This kind of generalized recreation service may also be found among the ancillary types associated with multi-function agencies. Separate unit centers like the Phoenix Center for the Blind and the Seattle Social Center for the Blind continually find that blind persons who need specialized recreation bring with them an interrelated host of significant problems, *viz.*, financial, physical, psychological, social, vocational and others. Knowledgeable counselling and referral assistance is an important aspect of the specialized recreation program. The recreation center milieu encourages activity, in groups or alone, in which members are prone to articulate and express their debilitating frustrations and problems. Meaningful diagnostic observation, reporting and helpful follow-up should be important aspects of center principles and objectives. This is the primary aspect of recreation function through which members may again be linked with the "outside," desegregated and re-integrated.

Whether the recreation service is part of a larger agency program or a separate organization, the quality of the intake function is important. The first contact has a unique flavor which may significantly influence later attitudes, adjustments and achievements. This is particularly true for newly blinded persons or those who have been socially isolated for a long time.

The content and the character of the initial interview depends upon whether the process is basically a registration procedure for membership admission, or an inquiry preliminary to a professional helping service. No superiority is implicit in either, so long as the type of interview is a practical function of the specified purposes of the center. Considering the nature and need of many of the persons who require specialized services, the mere acquisition of demographic data and activity preferences seems inadequate, insensitive and short-sighted. Nevertheless, at the point of intake there is a general delineation between the programs which are oriented toward social group work.

In the predominately education-recreation program the primary intake concerns usually are with personal identity, physical health and activity preferences. In the predominately social group work program, the intake content includes an explanation of why the individual has come to the center, life circumstances significant to the prospective member, and how the program can be effective in meeting individual needs.

Some center programs utilize both professional disciplines, recreation and social work and others. This demonstrates that when workers and programs are mature, sophisticated and secure, the art of helping includes many means and methods. A recreation program which disregards the inner needs of its participants is superficial and limited, even when it glitters with hustle and bustle. The meeting of surface interests soon leads to boredom and fatigue, and program stimulants in the form of "bread and circuses" compound the felonies committed in the name of good intentions. Similarly, social group programs which eschew concrete recreation activities, eventually degenerate into frustrating exercises in meaningless verbosity and confusing semantics.

In summary, while there is not, and there should not be a dichotomous cleavage between education-recreation and social work-group work, program emphasis should determine the nature and focus of intake with the best interests of the applicant the common denominator.

Food Service and Refreshments

The bread and circus motif has been emphasized sufficiently to make any and all specialized recreation center personnel pause to consider the purposes served by providing something to eat. In some centers, because of a long daily program, a main meal, lunch or supper, is an important activity. From a cost accounting point of view, this is a major activity because food procurement, storage and preparation, kitchen management and cooking, equipment, supplies and necessary housekeeping services are all very expensive. The meal therefore should serve clearly specified program aims. Unless there is careful evaluation of the "eating" activities, valuable center resources may be expended to defeat center objectives.

There are many positives and negatives in the consideration of whether to include lunch or supper in the program. The "pro" factors include the following: (1) For many members, a meal with one's associates in a recreation setting, and as a specific part of the schedule of activities, seems to promote wholesome congeniality and socialization. (2) Most members are in marginal economic circumstances, and for them, the meal represents a substantial monetary saving, a needed nutritional supplement, and a welcomed respite from the ever-demanding chores involved in meal procurement when one is blind and/or alone. (3) Even for the relatively few members financially able to purchase a restaurant meal, going out engenders too many anxieties and tensions, and involves many guiding problems, even in centers which are located in areas containing acceptable restaurants. (4) Dining is the one activity which groups all or most of the members in one assembly. Thus, it can be used for certain center announcements, activity notices, recognitions, and attendance notations for statistics and transportation home car assignments.

The "con" aspects of meal provision devolve around the subtle characterization of the members as dependent unfortunates in need. Despite screening, one needs to be ever watchful for the insidious staff member, paid or volunteer, whose behavior is tangible evidence of a basic fear of blindness and resultant pity, as he enthusiastically "feeds" them. The giving and receiving of food and refreshments may be equated emotionally with the giving and receiving of personal interest and affection. Frustrations, hostilities, and misunderstandings are inherent in the specialized setting, increasing the needs and susceptibilities of givers and receivers, and pauperizing both. The meal can become a demeaning activity which serves as a deterrent to the constructive meeting of member needs and center objectives. Then, indeed, are the physically blind being led by the emotionally blind along an ancient path—exploitation.

Programs more than five hours in length have to include a meal of some sort. Then, as a major activity it should be milked for every possible contribution to center purposes. Tone and atmosphere in the dining area are crucial. These are determined by the preparation, the quality and the quantity of the food; the manner in which the meals are served, and the general decor and decorum in the dining room, i.e., reasonable quiet, absence of bustle and tension, as well as a considerate relationship between the members and the servers. Although the partaking of food with one's friends promotes conviviality and friendship, the actual or fancied denial of anticipated food or service begets surprising impatience and irascibility.

Fees for Meals

In almost all centers, a nominal fee is charged for a meal, i.e., from thirty-five to sixty cents. This is, of course, a fraction of the actual cost. Implications of dependency are particularly strong when there is no charge, because of the association of free meals with the very poor and folks who are "down and out." Careful provisions should be made for the few members who cannot pay. A simple interview is enough to establish a member's financial difficulties, and arrangements can easily be made for him to have the meal tickets or other tokens used for payment. Sometimes, such simple inquiries have helped members to improve their home situations through referrals to appropriate public and private agencies in the community.

Dining Area

In the multi-function agencies, the food preparation and the eating areas are used also by other service units of the organization, e.g., the sheltered work shop, the vocational training group or by regular agency personnel. Usually, employees associated with the business and management functions of the entire organization have the overall responsibility for the operation of the food service facility, equipment and staff up to the point where the meal is ready for the recreation member. The recreation center responsibility usually begins with the procurement of meal servers. In some centers, high school students from honorary and service clubs faithfully and competently help to get the meal from the kitchen to the members. In other centers, paid part-time waitresses are used. Not infrequently, and unhappily, it becomes necessary for the regular staff to help with serving, especially during school holidays or examination week.

Formica top square tables for four or six members are advised. The tables should be arranged in straight line rows so that members can more easily find their own places. Mindful of some of the personal characteristics of the members, it is not surprising that old cronics want to sit together, and a seat at someone else's table is usurped at some peril. Reasonable anger is generally a wholesome reaction, especially in a handicapped person, and the understanding recreator with a little wit may use such situations to advantage. Kitchen-dining areas lend themselves to a multiplicity of uses for other activities, from cooking classes in the kitchen to singing and drama groups in the dining room. Assuming responsible leadership and good housekeeping, no usable area should be sacrosanct for one particular activity only.

Transportation

You are not really in the world unless you move in it. Restricted mobility is a primary intrinsic effect of visual deprivation. Movement is related not only to physical action but also to psychological and social vitality. Because of the awareness of the pervasive implications of movement, in connection with both the intrinsic and extrinsic effects of blindness, there is increased emphasis on developing positive attitudes toward and specific skills in independent travel indoors and outdoors, for all blind individuals, regardless of age, providing, of course, that they can navigate physically. A name has been given to the segment of rehabilitative learning and technology of travel, i.e., peripatology.

Unhappily, despite increased efforts and improved techniques, it is apparent that the large majority of specialized center members can not and/or will not travel independently. These are, after all, the older folks who need specialized services and who perforce represent less adequately adjusted individuals. Realistically, the rush and crush of big city travel is a challenging chore even for the sighted—and currently, there are so many neighborhoods in which travel after dark is hazardous, especially for women. In some urban areas, it has even become necessary to assist the member right to his apartment door. Some members with useful vision manage to come to the center during daylight hours but have to be transported home after dark. A few members without usable vision are able and willing to travel independently both ways.

For a blind person to negotiate a center island train or bus platform with but a cane or dog requires enormous courage, superior physical and mental abilities and impelling motivations. The blind individual who is enabled to risk his life and limb for the sake of his psychological integrity is much more than just pragmatic. Even the best blind travellers will gladly sacrifice a little time and/or ego for some common sense human guiding. At best, independent travel without vision is an unending obstacle course, and the terror of the subway tracks compels never a pause in concentration and attention.

Transportation provided via automobiles is therefore one of the most demanding program factors. Paid transportation costs range from one fifth to one third of the total operations budget. Membership attendance is directly related to available center transportation. The adequate functioning of organized and continuing recreation activities is almost completely dependent upon reliable transportation provided by the center. Obviously, blind individuals who are least adequate and mobile are most dependent and isolated and most in need of specialized services. Conversely, blind individuals who are able to travel independently are able to visit relatives, friends, local voluntary and commercial recreation establishments or just walk. The proportion of specialized center members who are unable to travel independently is usually higher than ninety percent.

Because of the high cost of transportation, almost all centers devote considerable time to recruiting transportation volunteers with or without cars. A study was made of how the six largest specialized recreation centers in New York City handled their transportation. It was found that even after forceful and concerted efforts, in which a staff member devoted full time to the task, each center reluctantly but realistically turned to the utilization of paid transportation for the bulk of the membership. Some of these centers have been able to supplement the paid cars with volunteer drivers for their agency cars. Some have regular assistance from local American Red Cross Motor Corps, Council of Jewish Women, Lions and other fraternal and service organizations. Occasionally, a sighted individual with his own car is used, provided he has or is willing to get the suggested minimum of $300,000 of required liability insurance.

More often than not, volunteer cars cannot be depended upon to provide regular weekly service. Such offers of help are more useful for occasional or special events. Innumerable factors cause cancellations, from mildly inclement weather to an appointment at the hairdresser's. Volunteer drivers have been able to find many reasons for future unavailability, after encountering some of the idiosyncratic behavior of some members who must ride in front, or who will not sit next to a particular person, or insist upon an opened or closed window.

Substitute drivers for cancellations can be planfully arranged, but often, the second line of service also becomes unavailable, and so on. The results are disappointed blind persons, an empty facility, and a staff with little to do but prepare for more of the same—and with some feeling of guilt and question.

Of course, there are some exceptions. Perhaps in a particular locale where community concern is high, volunteer transportation resources may be developed to provide the necessary regular service.

However, it may take a full-time worker to schedule the volunteer drivers and substitutes, if the organized program is large.

In the New York City centers, private limousine service has become the best answer for the organized specialized recreation centers. Most of the available private transportation services are similar. The cars hold seven persons, the maximum set by the state Public Service Commission. The cost per car ranges from fifteen to twenty dollars for a round trip, dependent upon the total distance travelled in getting the group to and from the center. The first person picked up, or the last person taken home, seldom rides longer than one hour.

Most members consider the car ride part of the recreation program and, on some trips, according to the drivers, members would benefit from the presence of a group worker. Because the private services are used regularly, the drivers become acquainted with the members and some of their personal needs, e.g., the need to ride in a particular part of the car, or to sit next to a certain member, or to be helped to a certain entrance of their residence.

The average round trip cost per member ranges from two to three dollars, determined by whether the car is full or riding with fewer than seven members due to absentees. Members are urged to notify the center in time to cancel their pick-up if they are not coming. Usually, several consecutive failures of this sort results in suspension of transportation for the member. Telephone and mail follow-ups are made by the recreation center, and/or a home visit from the social service department of the parent agency.

A program which averages fifty members in daily attendance will use approximately six cars to bring in members, and eight cars to take them home, including those who came in independently. The six round trip cars cost approximately one hundred and twenty dollars and the two extra home-only cars about twenty dollars, or a total of one hundred and forty dollars. For an organized recreation program which is open five days per week, the transportation costs come to seven hundred dollars per week. For a forty-week season, the transportation item comes to the tidy sum of $28,000,00. No wonder transportation is estimated at from one fifth to one third of the total budget of the specialized recreation center.

There is general agreement that such regularly provided transportation is fundamental to the purposeful and effective operation of the organized recreation programs in the specialized centers. Obviously, philosophy, principles, activities, leadership, administration, facilities and equipment are of no avail without members who need the specialized recreation service.

All kinds of solutions have been sought to lower transportation costs. Volunteer drivers are but little help. Relatives are almost completely unresponsive. So the centers turn to the members themselves. The members should be made aware of the problem and asked to consider meeting some or all of the cost of transportation. In some centers, all members are required to pay toward the cost unless they explicitly state their inability to do so. In the aforementioned New York City centers all members in receipt of public assistance must reimburse to the center the amount which the local Department of Welfare will include in their budgets upon request by the member and verification by the center. The Department of Welfare can include the actual estimated cost.

In 1960, when the specialized recreation centers were studied, the welfare transportation reimbursements, in the largest center, with a membership population of over one thousand, approximated twenty per cent of the total transportation, a significant sum. However, current blind welfare recipients are decreasing, as more and more older Americans become eligible for Social Security benefits. Voluntary contributions from members not on welfare amounted to less than one per cent of total cost.

The requirement that financially able members contribute toward the cost of their transportation is conducive to strengthening the member's feeling of independence. At least, he is given opportunity to decide whether he is able and willing to pay. Requiring all welfare recipients to obtain the allowance and reimburse it to the center is justified on the basis that it is incumbent upon the center to utilize all available community resources. Every effort should be made to safeguard, as far as possible, the confidential nature of these transactions. Some members are extremely reluctant to identify themselves as welfare recipients.

The high cost of necessary transportation is a serious and continuous concern for the specialized recreation center.

Fees and Charges

It is a fundamental sociological truism that prevalent social values which are distilled from the dynamic cultural matrix of mores and taboos are powerful determinants of human ideas and conduct. It is a fundamental psychological truism that an individual's concept of himself tends to conform to the expectant status and role which the surroundings decree for him.

Our culture is disturbingly materialistic. It is a reality that many of our value judgments are founded and expressed in money and material terms. Therefore, it is not surprising that so often, achievement and independence are evaluated in such a framework of values. "You get what you pay for," is the admonition of a repeated television commercial about coffee; but this notion subtly pervades our sense of objective and immanent worth. Price is associated with quality as well as quantity and that which is free is perforce inferior. Economic independence is so highly prized it often serves as the principal criterion of personality independence. Then, through the simplest syllogism in logic, this type of independence becomes an essential component of self-worth and dignity for society and the individual. This is our cultural reality: to be on your own and do for yourself is the essense of freedom and the road to selfrealization.

Blindness and dependence are almost synonymous terms. Social practices and sanctions confirm and strengthen the associational relationship. In and around the major specialized recreation centers in New York City, a blind person finds it almost impossible to directly pay for a specialized agency service or to directly purchase a braille book or periodical. Frequently enough, he is not allowed to pay for a drink in a bar, if he happens to behave as a blind person is expected to behave, i.e., needs a little help getting located. Blind persons are the only physically handicapped individuals who receive extra income tax exemptions, half fare concessions on many public carriers, and miraculously, a seat on a crowded New York City subway, if they happen to behave as a blind person is expected to behave, i.e., a little helpless bumping does it.

Of course, there is abundant data which show beyond question that blind persons are significantly disadvantaged economically.

Most of the enrolled members in the major specialized recreation centers in New York City are in receipt of public assistance, are being largely supported by relatives, or just getting along on social security pensions, with supplementary help from other sources. Nevertheless, whether on a full or partial basis, the sweetness of independence cannot be denied. To witness the pride and dignity which seems to emanate from a person's deepest innards, is an experience which forever weds one to an appreciation of the importance of self-determination.

At the least, there is dignity in being asked, and in being given an opportunity to declare oneself—even angrily if need be. *A priori* denial of the blindness-dependency stereotype is inherently self-strengthening and self-respecting for the members. Expecting most blind members to pay for recreation services is patently ridiculous; or even expecting some payment from all the members in favorable financial circumstances. "You raise money for us, why should we pay," has been put to many center workers in declaratory rather than question form. There is little to be gained from discussion with these members of the principles involved. The concern should be about the members, few or many, for whom payment for services and materials represents an opportunity for normality and linkage with an independent past, present and future.

Substituting and advocating voluntary donations from members is substantially a different matter and, in a sense, may be considered a hypocritical rationalization. The financial ability of the member is affirmed while he is denied the opportunity to directly pay for what he receives. The simultaneous position of donator and receiver of services is certainly more ambiguous than the one in which a member pays what he can for services rendered.

Fees and charges, which are continual and normal facts of everyday life in modern commercial society, can be considered from another point of view. Volunteers notwithstanding, specialized recreation service for blind adults is relatively expensive. Therefore, it is incumbent upon the center to utilize every community resource. The members are close and immediate resources. Members should be asked to help themselves to the extent that they are able—and is this not a proud slogan of purpose and objectives of the specialized centers, the specialized agencies, and work for the blind in general?

There is no gainsaying the fact that at times the administrative costs involved in the collecting and accounting of fees and charges may exceed the receipts. Efficient organization would seem to preclude such an eventuality, but even so, this is beside the issue. The basic concerns are with principles and practices which enhance the status and dignity of the members by giving them the opportunity to make a decision which concerns them and their program. Members need opportunities to express a sense of power and of approbation. Why not add this additional opportunity to program media? For even in deciding that one cannot or does not wish to pay, a member manifests some ego-power. It is not unusual to encounter a center member who needs to be at the center, yet strongly resents the necessity to be there on a dependent basis.

Lastly, it should be emphasized that regardless of administrative policy concerning fees and charges, the general climate within the specialized center has the nature and properties of a culture. All things, animate and inanimate, contribute toward the attitudes and values which pervade the atmosphere and determine the roles the members take. Empirical data persuasively suggests that in this specialized milieu, the knowledge that those members who can pay, may pay, is a positive factor in promoting and achieving avowed center objectives.

Some workers pose an interesting conjecture. If blind persons become too independent, who will want to help them? While this millennium is far from realization, the simple response is obvious. Independent persons who are blind will not need specialized services. Their recreation needs can be met in the regular recreation facilities provided in the community. Perhaps too often, the basic motivation for donations may be suspect for many of us seem to need dependents.

Specialized center programs include many areas of function which naturally and normally lead themselves to fee charging considerations, *viz.*, paid transportation, meals, equipment and materials (guitars, recorders, and harmonicas in music; kits and wool in arts and crafts).

If one gets what he pays for, what is paid for undoubtedly has more worth for the member. There is an enormous difference between member worth and member worthiness. The former notion respects and strengthens personality, the latter patronizes and demeans the individual.

SELECTED BIBLIOGRAPHY

Blindness: Definitions, Incidence and Prevalence

Hurlin, Ralph G.: Estimated prevalence of blindness in the United States and in the individual states, 1960. *Sight Saving Review, XXXII*: 4-12, Spring, 1962.

Kerby, Edith: *Manual on the Uses of the Standard Classification of Causes of Blindness.* Prepared for the Committee on Statistics of the Blind, American Foundation for the Blind, Inc., New York, 1940.

Social Security Act, Title X, Section 1017. Definitions, Paragraph (b).

U. S. Department of Health, Education, and Welfare, Public Health Service: *Proceedings, First Annual Conference of the Model Reporting Area for Blindness Statistics.* Public Health Service Publication No. 972, 1962.

Historical Perspectives in Work for the Blind

Farrell, Gabriel: *The Story of Blindness.* Cambridge, Mass., Harvard University Press, 1956.

French, Richard Slayton: *From Homer to Helen Keller.* New York, American Foundation for the Blind, Inc., 1932.

Ross, Ishbel: *Journey into Light.* New York, Appleton-Century Crofts, Inc., 1951.

Yahraes, Herbert: *What Do You Know About Blindness.* New York, Public Affairs Pamphlet No. 124, 1947.

Zahl, Paul A. (Ed.): *Blindness: Modern Approaches to the Unseen Environment.* Princeton, N. J., Princeton University Press, 1950.

Recreation and Recreation Needs

Danford, Howard G.: *Recreation in the American Community.* New York, Harper & Brothers, 1953.

Nash, Jay B.: *Philosophy of Recreation and Leisure.* St. Louis, C. V. Mosby Company, 1953.

Towle, Charlotte: *Common Human Needs.* National Association of Social Workers, 95 Madison Avenue, New York 16, N. Y., 1957.

Social Group Work

Ferguson, Elizabeth A.: *Social Work: An Introduction.* Philadelphia and New York, J. B. Lippincott Company, 1963.

Group Work with the Aged. Central Bureau for the Jewish Aged, 31 Union Square West, New York 3, N. Y., 1963.

Konopka, Gisela: *Social Group Work: A Helping Process.* Englewood Cliffs, N. J., Prentice-Hall, Inc., 1963.

Trecker, Harleigh B.: *Social Group Work: Principles and Practices.* New York, Whiteside, Inc., 1955.

Wilson, Gertrude, and Ryland, Gladys: *Social Group Work Practice.* Cambridge, Mass., Houghton Mifflin Company, 1949.

Specialized Services for Atypical Individuals

American Association of Workers for the Blind, Inc.: Proceedings. Washington, D. C., AAWB, Reports of Annual Conventions 1955-1964.

Department of Health, Education, and Welfare, Office of Vocational Rehabilitation: *Rehabilitation Centers for Blind Persons.* Rehabilitation Service Series No. 880, 1956.

Hunt, Valerie V.: *Recreation for the Handicapped.* New York: Prentice-Hall, Inc., 1955.

Langerhaus, Clara, and Redkey, Henry (Ed.): *Adjustment Centers for the Blind.* American Foundation for the Blind, Inc., 15 West 16th Street, New York 11, N. Y., 1951.

Miller, Irving, and Barr, Sherman: *Recreation Services for Deaf-Blind Persons.* New York, The Industrial Home for the Blind, 1959.

Thompson, Morton: *Starting a Recreation Program in Institutions for the Ill or Handicapped Aged.* New York, National Recreation Association, 1960.

The Why-What-and How of Recreation in the Medical Setting. Raleigh, North Carolina, North Carolina Recreation Commission, Bulletin No. 27, 1959.

The Impact of Blindness

Attitudes Toward Blindness. American Foundation for the Blind, 15 West 16th Street, New York 11, N. Y. Social Research Series No. 1, 1951.

Bauman, Mary K.: *Adjustment to Blindness.* Pennsylvania State Council for the Blind, Department of Welfare, 1954.

Barker, Roger G., *et al.*: *Adjustment to Physical Handicap and Illness: A Survey of the Social Psychology of Physique and Disability.* New

York, Social Science Research Council Bulletin 55, Revised 1953.

Carroll, Rev. Thomas J.: *Blindness*. Boston, Little, Brown and Co., 1961.

Chevigny, Hector, and Braverman, Sydell: *The Adjustment of the Blind*. New Haven, Yale University Press, 1950.

Cholden, Louis S.: *A Psychiatrist Works With Blindness*. New York, American Foundation for the Blind, 1958.

Cutsforth, Thomas D.: *The Blind in School and Society*. New York, American Foundation for the Blind, Inc., 1951.

Fitting, Edward A.: *Evaluation of Adjustment to Blindness*. American Foundation for the Blind, 15 West 16th Street, New York 11, N. Y., Research Series No. 2, 1954.

Gowman, Alan G.: *The War Blind in American Social Structure*. New York, American Foundation for the Blind, Inc., 1957.

Himes, Joseph S., Jr.: Changing Attitudes of the Public Toward the Blind. *The New Outlook for the Blind, LII* (9):330-335, November, 1958.

The I.H.B. Way: An Approach to the Rehabilitation of Blind Persons. The Industrial Home for the Blind, 57 Willoughby Street, Brooklyn 1, N. Y., 1961.

Meyerson, Lee: Somatopsychological Aspects of Blindness, *Psychological Diagnosis and Counseling of the Adult Blind*. Edited by Wilma Donahue. New York, American Foundation for the Blind, Inc., 1947, pp. 12-34.

Raskin, Nathaniel J.: *The Living Expenses of Blind Persons*. American Foundation for the Blind, 15 West 16th Street, New York 11, N. Y., Research Series No. 4, 1955.

The Activity Program

The Athletic Institute: *The Recreation Program*. Chicago, 1954.

Butler, George D.: *Introduction to Community Recreation*. New York, McGraw Hill Book Company, Inc. 2d ed., 1947; 3rd ed., 1959.

Bucher, Charles A.: *Methods and Materials in Physical Education and Recreation*. St. Louis, The C. V. Mosby Company, 1954.

Buell, Charles E.: *Active Games for the Blind*. Ann Arbor, Michigan, Edwards Brothers, Inc., 1953.

Frampton, Merle E.: *Education of the Blind*. New York, World Book Company, 1940.

Gabrielsen, M. Alexander, Betty Spears, and B. W. Gabrielsen: *Aquatic Handbook*. Englewood Cliffs, N. J., Prentice-Hall, Inc., 1960.

Leonhard, Charles: *Recreation through Music*. New York, A. S. Barnes and Company, 1952.

Ritter, Charles G.: *Hobbies of Blind Adults.* American Foundation for the Blind, 15 West 16th Street, New York 11, N. Y., Education Series—No. 7, 1953.

Stafford, George T.: *Sports for the Handicapped.* New York, Prentice-Hall, Inc., 1950.

Leadership and Volunteers

Corbin, H. Dan: *Recreation Leadership.* New York, Prentice-Hall, Inc., 1954.

Industrial Home for the Blind: *The I.H.B. Volunteer Manual.* Brooklyn, N. Y., 1960.

Kraus, Richard: *Recreation Leader's Handbook.* New York, McGraw Hill Book Company, Inc., 1955.

Personnel Practices for Recreation Departments and Agencies. American Recreation Society, Inc., 1404 New York Avenue, N.W., Washington 5, D. C., 1959.

Personnel Standards in Community Recreation Leadership. National Recreation Association, 8 West Eighth Street, New York 11, N. Y., 1957.

Shapiro, Robert, and Saul, Shura: Effective Use of Volunteers in Group Work and Recreation Programs. *The New Outlook for the Blind, LIII* (10):361-366, 1959.

Administration: Site and Facilities

American Standards Specifications for Making Buildings and Facilities Accessible to, and Usable by, the Physically Handicapped. New York, American Standards Company, 1961.

Meyer, Harold D., and Brightbill, Charles K.: *Recreation Administration.* Englewood Cliffs, N. J., Prentice-Hall, Inc., 1956.

Planning a Community Recreation Building. National Recreation Association, 8 West Eighth Street, New York 11, N. Y., 1960.

Schedule for the Appraisal of Community Recreation. National Recreation Association, 8 West Eighth Street, New York 11, N. Y., 1957.

Research and Evaluation

How'm I Doing—Chart for Recreation Play Directors. California, City of Long Beach Recreation Commission, July, 1955 (mimeographed).

Leisure Activities Study. American Foundation for the Blind, 15 West 16th Street, New York 11, N. Y., May 1961.

The Middletown Lighthouse for the Blind: A Survey. New York, The

American Foundation for the Blind, Inc., Studies in Community Planning, No. 1, 1957.

Nineteen Recreation Principles. National Recreation Association, 8 West Eighth Street, New York 11, N. Y., undated.

Organization and Administration of Agency Volunteer Service Program. Welfare and Health Council of New York City, Central Volunteer Bureau, 44 East 23rd Street, New York 10, N. Y., 1954.

INDEX

A

Accidents, 162
Accountability, 156
Accreditation, 133
Achievement, 87
  frustrations, 65
Activities, 45
  categories, 45
  novel, 47
  people-centered, 46
  recognition, 50
  rewards, 49
  selection, 46
Adaptations, 25, 46, 172
  adjustment mechanisms, 21, 30, 35, 87
Administration, 131, 177
  definition, 147
A.F.B. bulletin No. 13,
  legislation series, 37
Agencies serving the blind, 10
Amateur radio, 126, 127
Ambivalence, 192
Altruism, 137
American Association for Health,
  Physical Education and Recreation, 48
American Association of Workers for
  the Blind, 20, 145
American Blind Bowlers Association, 108
American Foundation for the Blind, 146
American Recreation Journal, 146
American Recreation Society, 48, 144
American Red Cross Motor Corps, 187
American Shuffleboard Company, 120
American standards specifications for
  making buildings and facilities usable
  by the handicapped, 160
Anagrams, 118
Anxiety, 35
Appraisal of community recreation, 162
Arts and crafts, 49
  class size, 65
  materials, 65
Athletic institute, 48, 158
Auspices, 169
  autocratic, 170
Autoharp, 96

B

Bag punching, 47
Ball, Edith L., viii
Bands, 96
Banquets, 105
Bardin-La Follette act, 11
Barker, Roger G., 30
Barr, Sherman, 37
Basketry, 51
Beauty, 174
Beauty culture, 125
Beggar, 31
Behavior characteristics, 24, 36, 43, 76, 181
Behavior observation, 130, 181
Bingo, 107
Blind in school and society, 27
Blindness, 4
  definition, 5
  effects, 25, 26, 28, 36, 37
  forecast, 3
  legal, 5
Blind staff, 150
Board of directors, 147, 176
Boredom, 182
Bowl-ball, 129
Bowling, 108
  averages, 109
  guide rail, 110
  instruction, 111
  leagues, 108
Braille, 42, 88, 108, 114, 132
Braille, Louis, 9
Brainstorming, 129
Bread and circuses, 14, 73, 105, 154, 182

Bridge, 115
Brooklyn Bureau of Social Services and Children's Aid Society, 134
Bureau of Labor Stastics, 36
Bumper pool, 113
Butler, George D., 19

C

Camp lighthouse, 104, 122
Camps, 103
Canoeing, 103, 104
Canteen, 106
Cards, 114
Carnivals, 105
Carroll, Thomas J., 35, 139
Carron Industries, Inc., 129
Carry-over values, 171
Case, Maurice, 167
Ceramics, 54
Ceremonies, 127
Charges, 40, 41, 102, 190
Checkers, 117
Chess, 116
Chevigny, Hector, 28
Chlorination, 121
Cholden, Milton S., 30
Choruses, 96
Clubs, 126
  brainstorming, 129
  special interest, 128
Code of ethics, 179
Co-education, 40
Colleges, 136
Commission on Standards and Accreditation of Services for the Blind, 133
Common problems, 42
Communication, 91
  deaf-blind, 132
Community, 70
  emissaries, 70
  links, 70
  organization, 169
Community needs, xiii
Community resources, 101, 122, 172, 191
Compensation, 25, 31
Congressional House Sub-Committee on Special Education, 37
Consciousness of kind, 41
Consultation, 172
Contraction, 32
Control, 34
Council of Jewish Women, 187
Creativity, 54
Crises, 25, 34
Cutsforth, Thomas D., 27

D

Dance, 69
  eurythmics, 70
  folk, 71
  music, 75
  partners, 74
  social, 73
  square, 72
Deaf-blind, 37, 132
Debates, 90
Debilitation, 43
Dedication, 134, 144, 151
Deductions, 8
Defenses, 87
Democratic, 170
Dependency, 21, 34, 43
Dermo-optical perception (D.O.P.), 25
Desegregation, 182
Destructiveness, 86
Diagnostic, 130, 181
Diderot, Denis, 8
Diets, 39
Discipline comparisons, 23
Disturbances, 42
Dominoes, 118
Donahue, Wilma, 36
Donations, 65, 129
Dramatics, 76
  applause, 77
  audiences, 79
  improvisations, 78
  lighthouse players, 79
  members selection, 80
  physical orientation, 78
  play production, 78, 79
  play selection, 81
  self-revelation, 77
  staffing, 82
  supervision, 84
  workshops, 77
Dyno-Mite Tapewriter, 89

E
Economics, 40
Ego, 24
Ego impaired, 44
Ego power, 192
Ego strengthening, 20, 41
Elizabethan Poor Laws, 8
Emergencies, 39, 175
Environmental control, 20, 34
Equipment, 149
Essay on blindness, 8
Eurythmics, 70
Evaluation, 141, 142, 165, 166, 174, 180
Exceptional behavior, 39
Executive director, 148, 177
Exhibits, 47, 79
Exploitation, 47, 184, 190, 192
Extrinsic effects of blindness, 26, 30, 35

F
Facilities, 158
  adaptations, 159
  cleaning, 165
  multiple use, 159
Failure, 71, 95
Fairs, 105
Fees, 40, 102, 156, 184, 190
  budget, 41
  self determination, 41
Fencing, 47
Field work, 136
Financial statuses, 40
Financing, 154, 155, 156
  per capita costs, 155
  public funds, 156
Finger painting, 47
Fire drills, 164
First aid, 125, 163
Folk dancing, 71
Folk songs, 98
Food, 174
Food service, 183
Forecast, 3
Foreign languages, 90
Forums, 90
French, Richard Slayton, 25
Freud, 9
Frustrations, 95
Fund raising, 155, 156, 179

G
Gabrielsen, Milton A., ix
Games, 106
Gardening, 129
Genius, 31
Glee clubs, 97
Gowman, Alan G., 32
Grimacing, 43
Groping, 43
Group activities, 84
Group definition, 84
Group dynamics, 84
Group destructiveness, 87
Group leadership, 86
Group negatives, 85, 86
Group peers, 87
Group projects, 50
Group social work, 85, 86
Group special interests, 85
Group supervision, 86
Group values, 84, 85
Guitar, 98, 100
Gymnastics, 112

H
Habitation, 43
Ham radio, 126, 127
Handicrafts, 49
Haptic, 49
Hauy, Valentine, 8
Hayes, Samuel P., 27
Health, 39
Helping service, 182
Himes, Joseph S., Jr., 12, 30
Hiring, 149
History, 7
Holistic, 17
Home nursing, 125
Homeostasis, 24
Homer, from, to Helen Keller, 25
L'Hopital des Quinze-Vingts, 7
Hostilities, 184
Household tensions, 45
Housekeeping, 164
How'm I Doing Chart, 141, 166

I
Illinois, 163
Immobilization, 42

Improvisation, 78
Incidence, 3
Indigenous leadership, 126, 154, 171
Individualization, xii, 23, 24, 153, 169
Industrial Home for the Blind, 13
In-service training programs, 145, 149, 180
L'Institution National des Jeunes Aveugles, 8
Insurance, 122
Intake, 46, 181, 182
Integration, 171, 182
Interaction, 21
Inter-faith, 42
Inter-racial, 42
Intervention, professional, 22
Intrinsic effects, 26, 30, 35
Isolation, 14, 32, 154

K

Keller, Helen, 10
Keller, Helen, from Homer to, 25
Kerby, Edith, 4
Kilns, 57
King Louis IX, 7
Knok-hockey, 129, 130

L

Languages, 87, 90
Laughter, 46
Leadership, 48, 131, 175
  indigenous, 126, 154, 171
  inferiority, 22
  qualifications, 131, 132
  trained, 22
Leather, 62
Lectures, 90
Leisure, vii
Leonhard, Charles, 94
Liability, 122
Library, 180
Lighthouse, 13
Lighthouse players, 79
Linguistics, 87
Limitations, 27
Lindeman, Edward C., 134
Links, 69, 87, 113, 122, 171, 182, 191
Lions clubs, 117, 118
Literary, 87
Looms, 51
Lounge, 106
Lowenfeld, Berthold, 27

M

Maintenance, 164
  cleaning, 165
Manual accomplishments, 49
Manual alphabet, 132
Manual for The Operation Of Recreation Programs In Specialized Centers For Blind Adults, 167
Manual on the Uses of Standard Classification of Causes of Blindness, 4
Marginality, 40
Marx Script Writing Board, 91
Mass gatherings, 154, 171
Mechanisms of adjustment, 21, 87
Medical, 39
Member age, 38
Member ambivalence, 192
Member attendance, 152
Member dignity, 192
Member donations, 191
Member economics, 190
Member physical examinations, 163, 174
Member public assistance, 191
Member sex, 39
Memorials, 127
Metal, 62
Myerson, Lee, 36
Milieu, 39, 171, 185, 192
Miller, Irving, 37
Millinery, 64
Misrepresentation, 47
Mobility, 42, 69, 94, 125, 153, 154, 172, 185, 186
Moon-type, 92
Mosaics, 67
Mutiple handicaps, 35
Murray, H. A., 16
Music, 94
  appreciation, 99
  community sings, 97
  vocational, 96

N

Nash, Jay B., 16
National Association of Social Workers, 145
National Catholic Welfare Council, 48

National Industries for the Blind, 11
National Institute for the Blind, 91
National Institution for the Young Blind, 8
National Jewish Welfare Board, 48
National origin, 41
National Recreation Association, 48, 145, 159
National Water Ski Association, 123
Nature, 101
Needs, 16, 17, 18, 19
  basic, 16
  community, xiii
  physiologic, 16
  psychogenic, 17
  recreation, 17, 18, 19
  specialized center, 12
New outlook for the blind, 141
New York Association for the Blind, 160, 161
New York Jewish Guild for the Blind, 12
New York University, 167
Non-professional staff, 151
Normality, 39

O

Objectives, 148, 168, 177
Observations, 130, 181
Orientation, 114, 126
Oscar Schmidt International, Inc., 96
Outings, 101, 113

P

Partial sight, 5, 37
Participant achievement, 171
Participant economic status, 172
Participant evaluation, 174
Participant mobility, 175
Participant orientation, 175
Parties, 105
Part time staff, 131
Patrons (Patronizers), 97, 98
Peer relationships, 87
Perception, 4, 25
Peripatology, 94, 186
Personality, 24
Personnel practices, 150
Phoenix Center for the Blind, 154, 181
Phonographs, 128
Physicals, 35, 39
Physique, 24
Pisart Script Writing Board, 92, 93
Planning, 48, 148
Planning a community recreation building, 159
Play productions, 79
Plays, 83
Poker, 114
Pool, 113
Pool (Bumper), 113
Pools, swimming, 121
Pot holders, 53
Potters' wheel, 58
Poverty, 40
Prevalence, 3
Principles, 44
Principles of operation, 167
  philosophy, 167, 168
  validity of specialized institution, 168
  visual impairment, 168
Prizes, 108
Problems (common), 42
Professional intervention, 22
Professionalization, 179, 180
Professional Recreation, 65, 144
Program, 45
  activities, 45
  adaptations, 38
  age, 40
  autocratic, 170
  beauty, 174
  co-educational, 40
  contrivance, 38
  daily, 153
  democratic, 170
  disturbance, 42
  emergencies, 175
  individualization, 46
  isolation, 154
  mass activities, 154
  membership participation, 105
  milieu, 192
  objectives, 20, 168, 169
  organized, 20
  people-centered, 130
  planning, 153
  rewards, 87
  season, 151

statistics, 156
summer, 103
time, 152, 173
variety, 173
Psychiatrists, 28, 30
Psychoanalytic, 28
Psychocultural, 35
Psychodrama, 76, 77
Psychology, 27
Psychosexual, 36
Psychotherapy, 39
Public assistance, 40, 191
Public education, 179
Public funds, 172
Publicity, 135, 179
Public relations, 79, 149, 162

Q

Queen of the senses, 24

R

Race, 41
Raffia, 51
Randolf-Sheppard Act, 11
Reading groups, 90
Recognition, 143
Records, 156
activity cards, 157
case records, 157
group work, 157
intake, 157
recreation, 157
Recreation Committee of the City of Long Beach, California, 141
Recreation, deaf-blind, 37
Recreation definition, 15
Recreation experiences, 105
Recreation magazines, 141
Recreation organized, 48
Recreation profession, 14, 15, 65, 144
Recreation through music, 94
Recruitment, 136
Referrals, 172, 181
Refreshments, 106, 174, 183
Rehabilitation, 43
Religion, 41
Religious activities, 126
Religious festivals, 127
Remuneration, 132
Reorganization, adjustment, 30, 35
Reports, 156
Research, 136
Reversal role, 74
Rhythm bands, 99
Role reversal, 74
Roles, 31, 35, 87
Roller skating, 113
Ross, Ishbel, 11, 36
Royal Bank of Canada, 134
Rug making, 53

S

Safety, 162, 172
emergencies, 164
Saint Louis (King Louis IX), 7
Schedule for the appraisal of community recreation, 162
Schools for the blind, 9
Scrabble, 118
Scrap materials, 149
Script writing, 91, 92, 93
signatures, 92
writing board, 92, 93
Scuba diving, 47, 104, 121, 122
Sculpture, 59
Seattle Social Center for the Blind, 155, 181
Self, 25, 34
Self-deceit, 83
Self-determination, 41, 191
Self-risk, 43, 49
Senses, 49
Sensory impact, 25, 26
Sensory substitutes, 49, 174
Sewing, 64
Sex, 39, 40
Shelter, 7
Sheltered employment, 10
Shuffleboard, 119
Singing, 96
Site, 158
Skating, 114
Skin-diving, 104, 122
Smoking, 75
Social adjustment, 31
Social dances, 73
Social events, 105
Social group work, 20, 39
Social group worker, 86

Social institutions, 15
Sociality, 69, 105
Socialization, 88
Social Science, 29, 30, 36
Social Security Act, 4, 11
Social work, 14, 85
Social Work Journal, 146
Sociologist, 30
Sociology, 26, 190
Somatopsychology, 36
Songs, 174
Special interest groups, 85
Specialization, xiii
Specialized agency services, 36, 162
Sports, 106
Square dancing, 72
Staff, 178
  blind, 150
  development, 145
  hourly wages, 133
  in-service training, 145, 180
  non-professional, 151
  paid, 131
  part time, 133
  qualifications, 150
  recruitment, 132
  remuneration, 150
  salaries, 133, 151, 178, 179, 180
  supportive, 151
Standards, 170
Starting a recreation program in institutions for the ill or handicapped aged, 38
State aid, 9
Statistics, 156, 163
Status, 31, 33
Subculture, 42
Summer programs, 103
Supervisees, 149
Supervision, 151, 165
Supplies, 149
Swimming, 120

T

Table games, 106, 114
Tactility, 49
Talking book, 128
Tape recording, 128
Television, 106
Tensions, 35
Thompson, Morton, vii, 38, 158
Tiling, 67
Title X, 11
Trained leadership, 22
Transportation, 43, 158, 173, 185, 186, 188, 189
  American Red Cross Motor Corps, 187
  contributions, 189
  costs, 101, 188
  Council of Jewish Women, 187
  fees, 189
  insurance, 187
  public funds, 189
  volunteers, 187
Travel, 42, 94
Treatment centers, 39
Trecker, Harleigh B., 21
Trips, 102
TV, 106
Typing, 91

U

Ukelele, 98
Uneasiness, 35
Usable vision, 5

V

Values, 190
Venetian blind script writing board, 91
Vision, 37
Visual acuity, 4, 5
Visual efficiency, 25
Visual impairment, 37
Visual perception, 25
Volunteers, 14, 47, 134, 170, 176
  apprehensions, 70
  assignments, 70
  attitudes, 136
  board of directors (trustees), 147
  dedication, 134
  evaluation, 140
  level of service, 135
  motivations, 137
  neuroticisms, 184
  orientation, 138
  recognition, 143
  record cards, 157
  recruitment, 70, 135

relationships, 139
screening, 136
specialized, 125
supervision, 139
training, 137, 138, 140

W

Wagner-O'Day Act, 11
Water-skiing, 123, 124
Weaving, 51
Woodwork, 66
Worchel, Philip, 28, 29
Workshops, 77
Writing guides, 91, 92, 93
Marx board, 91
Venetian blind, 91

Y

Young Men's and Women's Christian Associations, 48